Ultimate Gift Experiences

Ultimate Gift Experiences

Your guide to unusual, adventurous and once in a lifetime gifts

Compiled by Steve Shipside

First published in 2007 by

The Infinite Ideas Company Limited
36 St Giles
Oxford, OX1 3LD
United Kingdom
www.infideas.com

Direct Experiences Ltd.
Mallory Park Circuit
Kirkby Mallory
Leicestershire, LE9 7QE
www.directexperiences.co.uk

A CIP catalogue record for this book is available from the British Library

ISBN 10: 1-904902-53-7
ISBN 13: 978-1-904902-53-9

Text and cover designed by Cylinder

Typeset by Sparks, Oxford – www.sparks.co.uk

Printed and bound in Italy

Contents

Introduction

We all know how difficult it can be to come up with original, exciting and thoughtful gifts. Many of us have also had the experience of trying to book something new and interesting for a particular event such as a hen or stag do, company day out or special birthday party. We can often spend hours dragging ourselves around the high street shops or searching on the internet only to come up with a gift that doesn't quite hit the mark, or book an event when we're not really sure what we're letting ourselves in for.

Well now the years of fruitless searching are over – *Ultimate Gift Experiences* is the solution to your dilemmas.

Infinite Ideas (www.infideas.com) and Direct Experiences (www.directexperiences.co.uk) are pleased to bring you the ultimate in gift experiences. We've trawled the length and breadth of the British Isles to bring you the very best suppliers out there across a broad range of activities and events. All the suppliers in this book have been chosen for their expertise in the industry and their ability to give you an experience to remember – they are regarded as the best in their various fields. This unique book is the ideal reference when you're stuck for gift ideas or simply want to treat yourself to an unusual day out.

So what can you expect to find inside? Well, first of all the book is divided into sections by type of experience so that you can decide which type of activity you're interested in. Suppliers are listed by region at the start of the section so that you can see at a glance which suppliers operate in your preferred area. To whet your appetite and give you a better idea of what to expect from your chosen event, course, attraction or activity, each section begins with a short article about the experiences in question. If you already know exactly what you're interested in then you can start with our comprehensive directory at the back, which will take you to all the suppliers that provide your chosen experience.

The detailed listings, by supplier, will provide you with all the information you need to book your chosen experience. Unlike other event suppliers we put you in touch directly with the supplier, so that if you have any queries, uncertainties or special requirements you can talk directly to the people offering the activity in question. All the companies listed are experts in the activities they provide and members of their relevant trade organisations, so you can book with them secure in the knowledge that you are purchasing a top-class experience at great value for money.

Great savings and free experience for every reader

The most exciting aspect of this book, however, is the opportunity to save money. The majority of the 120 suppliers listed are offering exclusive discounts to readers of *Ultimate Gift Experiences.* You can take advantage of as many of these offers as you like, so by booking experiences with just one or two suppliers you can recoup more than the cost of the book. In addition to this there is a free high speed passenger ride in a car, worth £30, with every copy of the book (see page 184 for your voucher).

With a wide range of experiences, from sporty thrills to spectator events, viewing art to creating it yourself, there is something in here for everybody, from 8 to 80. All levels of ability are catered for so whether you want a relaxing day out, would like to learn a new skill or are looking for physical challenges and thrills, *Ultimate Gift Experiences* holds the key.

Off-road

'The guy who invented the first wheel was an idiot. The guy who invented the other three, he was a genius.'

SID CAESAR, ACTOR AND WRITER

Roaring off-roading

Taking a look around town you could be mistaken for thinking that four-wheel drive is mainly used to overcome the hazards of Tesco's car park. Why not find out what it's really all about?

Off-roading is the perfect combination of adulthood and childhood. When you were a kid you loved mud. Boy or girl, it doesn't matter – fun had a name and that name was 'mud'. Getting dirty didn't mean anything shameful, it was just pure unadulterated fun and it drove mum and dad wild. Then you get older and you're no longer allowed to play in the mud but as a consolation prize you do get to play with big shiny toys like cars. Then someone has the brilliant idea that you can combine both – and it's fun for all the family because this time mum and dad just drive wildly.

Off-road adventures come in many shapes and sizes, from nippy little quad bikes to the full 56 tons of a Chieftain main battle tank. What they all have in common is a blend of raw fun, skills to learn, and an insight into just what extreme machines can really do when they're let out of the box and allowed to run wild. With *you* inside.

If you've got a 4×4 and fancy finding out what it can really do, then a day's off-roading tuition will blow you away. Gullies, holes, slopes like ski ramps – and yes, mud – all await you along with a deeply patient instructor (they have to be) who will teach you what diff lock really does and how it's about to make the difference between driving across the course and having to abandon ship as the Land Rover disappears beneath the waves.

The good news is that you get to make your mistakes with someone on hand to help when you realise that you're just not going to make it up that slope after all. A really good off-roading lesson opens up whole new worlds as it gives you a glimpse into the astonishing abilities of 4×4s. Of course it's just as likely to show up the limits of the driver but what the hell, it's not your car.

Quad riding aficionados will probably insist that quadding involves just as much skill. But they're wrong. The whole point of quads is that any idiot can get on one and go tearing off amongst the trees. Quad biking is all the adrenaline of motorbiking but with a wheel on each corner and slightly less falling off. Oh, and did I mention the mud?

But for the full off-road experience you're best off dispensing with wheels altogether. Once upon a time if you wanted to drive military vehicles you had to sign up for the army and get shot at as part of the package. Now anyone can have a go.

Tanks for the memories

Since you are unlikely to be lucky enough to have your own tank this means using someone else's. The rule of hired cars applies here, which is that any car is a 4×4 as long as it doesn't belong to you. The only difference is that with the military vehicles it's actually impossible to drive them so badly that you damage the vehicle. Proving this point is half the fun.

Tank driving days usually involve a variety of vehicles leading up the grand finale. These might include amphibious trucks, Ferret armoured cars, tracked armoured personnel carriers and self-propelled guns, all of which are great, but you know the real deal only comes with the big daddy of them all: the main battle tank.

Tank driving venues can usually be spotted by the total absence of anything to destroy. James Bond's *GoldenEye* put a glint in the eye of every amateur tank driver and made masonry nervous so you're unlikely to see so much as an outhouse worth careering off for. To make up for this the tank specialists usually offer a highlight in which someone gets to drive the tank over a normal car in return for supplemental cost. By this token you may want to have a few pints at lunchtime with the instructor and find out how much extra they charge to let you charge the Chieftain up the high street and through Tesco. You know you want to.

Tanks-A-Lot

Tanks-A-Lot holds a stock of over 100 military vehicles and runs from its own venue, and has operated for 14 years. Its most popular public day is 'The Full Monty' day. We organise the best military themed corporate events and get involved in film and TV work, and organise SAS themed overnight events for smaller parties. We also have our own road-legal stretched limo tank for special events.

Activity Location:
Northants

Booking/Contact details:
TANKS-A-LOT
T: 01295 768400
E: info@tanks-alot.co.uk
W: www.tanks-alot.co.uk

Practical Information:
Suitable clothing required for getting wet and dirty, boots or stout footwear essential

Equipment
Overalls can be provided
Combat camouflaged suits, safety helmets and goggles supplied where activity demands

Gift Vouchers:
Gift Vouchers available for a range of activities, but with a discount by booking direct

Special Offer/Incentive:
A 10% discount is available to readers. Please mention Direct Experiences when booking. Cannot be combined with any other special offer, promotion or discount.

Experiences:

The Full Monty:
Your day begins with registration, role call and safety briefing. You will then be issued with a camouflage suit and helmet. Typically, each team will compete in six of the following activities:

- Driving a 432 Armoured Personnel Carrier
- Driving a Lance Missile Carrier
- 18th-century flintlock and mortar firing
- SAS woodland patrol
- Driving an Abbot Gun Tank
- Driving a Hagglund Bv206
- Firearms and terrorism lecture

Plus the Full Monty winner will have the chance to drive a 56-ton Chieftain main battle tank ... over a saloon car! Life will never be the same again! We also offer a selection of SAS Mini Event Days including:

- Survival training
- Anti-tank
- Introduction to weapons
- Sniper alley

Tanks-A-Lot also offers an *After Dinner Speaking* service featuring two former members of the SAS, Britain's elite Special Forces. They will fascinate and amaze you with terrifying tales – of the Iranian Embassy siege in London, Iraq one and Falklands war jungle. These boys are the real deal, eloquent, witty, and jovial but also experts in the horror of war. They can bring with them an array of inert weapons and ordinance as props – from a claymore to a Chieftain tank!

★ 10% DISCOUNT
Please mention Direct Experiences when booking

Xtreme Offroad

Driving skills and judgement will be tested during this action-packed experience, on a 250 acre site on the Mendip Hills. Differing terrains include woodland, grass covered open cast mine workings and 3 large quarry areas for rock crawling. Whatever the level of driving skill, this experience ensures an exciting adrenaline filled day.

Activity Location:
South West

Contact details:
Xtreme Offroad
T: 01934 741582
E: info@xtremeoffroad.co.uk
W: www.xtremeoffroad.co.uk

Practical Information:
Each vehicle carries a maximum of four people

Gift Vouchers:
Vouchers are redeemable for a period of six months on the first Saturday of every month

Special Offer/Incentive:
A 10% discount will be applied for a booking of four or more people.

★ 10% DISCOUNT
For bookings of four or more people

Experiences:

4x4 Safari – Exploration:
Not driven off-road before? Now's your chance to learn how to make the most of the true capabilities of vehicles designed to cope with the ever-changing off-road terrain.

Accompanied by one of our senior instructors you will be taught the basic techniques that will enable you to safely take on our Jungle Exploration.

Activity time: 2 hours; driving time per person: 2x15 minutes.

4x4 Safari – Adventure:
Combining the jungle exploration with a chance to experience the challenge of loose stone on our very own quarry, you'll need to call upon your new-found skills if you are to make it out unaided.

Activity time: 3 hours; driving time per person: 3x15 minutes.

4x4 Safari – Camel Trophy Experience:
An opportunity to drive a genuine Camel Trophy Discovery through jungle, quarry and forest terrain encountering ever more difficult challenges. You will experience something of what it must have been like to compete in the toughest adventure of them all. Can you handle the challenge?

Activity time: 4 hours; driving time per person: 4x15 minutes.

Drive Tech Limited

Drive Tech Limited operates within the grounds of the Castle Combe Race Circuit, Chippenham, Wiltshire. We have been providing driving activities for over 18 years and specialise in skid control, 4×4 off-road driving and 200cc outdoor karting. We can accommodate individuals, small or large groups, birthday parties, stag & hen parties and corporate team-building/staff incentives.

Experiences:

Skid Control Training

Defensive Driver Training course aiming to teach full licence holders how to control a vehicle in icy or slippery road conditions. Our ADI instructors (or equivalent) teach a three hour course in our vehicles (front and rear wheel drive) all the disciplines required in a group learning environment. The course is both informative *and* excellent fun.

4×4 Off-Road Driving

Learn the skill of off-road driving in our Land Rover Discoveries with our BORDA (British Off-Road Driving Association) accredited instructors. Tough, but user-friendly course aiming to teach all the techniques used in 4×4 driving. Full driving licence required.

200cc Outdoor Karting

Exhilarating fun in 200cc Honda karts on a 350m outdoor track, with 'grippy' SMA tarmac surface giving you both speed and control. Grand Prix formats for individuals and groups on our public kart Grand Prix, which run most Saturday afternoons. Private events available for exclusive use groups in either Endurance or GP formats.

Also Junior Kart Racing School on 1st & 3rd Sunday mornings for 10-15 year olds (min 4' 8" in height).

Activity Location:
South West

Contact Details:
Drive Tech Ltd
T: 01249 783010
E: info@combe-events.co.uk
W: www.combe-events.co.uk

Corporate:
Tailored to individual requirements and budget. Please contact us for further information

Special Offer/Incentive:
10% discount off our 4×4 off-road driving course and/or 10% off when purchasing 2 adult kart gift vouchers.
Vouchers valid for 18 months from date of purchase.
Quote reference DE/DTECH06 when booking.

★ **10% DISCOUNT** (see text)
When you quote REF: DE/DTECH06

Quad Safari

Experience the thrill of quad biking and off-road 4×4 driving. Sites within easy reach of London, Reading and Cambridge.

Christmas, birthdays, anniversaries, reward, incentive, graduations, corporate gifts, Valentine's day! Looking for a gift? Stuck for ideas?

Quad biking safaris and Off-road 4×4 'Dream Drive' vouchers are 'open dated' so you don't need to worry about arranging a date in advance.

Activity Location:
South East

Contact details:
Quad Safari
T: 01920 822977
E: info@quadsafari.co.uk
W: www.quadsafari.co.uk

Practical Information:
Min. age 18 yrs
Protective clothing issued
Safety briefing for all participants

Gift Vouchers:
Available

Corporate Booking:
Corporate bookings can take place at Quad Safari site in Herts, a chosen venue or we can source a venue for you. A wide range of corporate events are available. Contact 01920 822 220 for further details.

Experiences:

Introductory Quad Safari:
Experience the thrill of quad biking. Training takes place over level ground around a marked circuit. As you gain experience you will feel able to increase your speed enabling you to power slide the quad bike around the turns. Subject to riders' ability and time there may also be an opportunity to venture across woodland tracks and steep slopes on the quad bike trail. Minimum age for this session is 14.

Half Day Quad Bike Safari:
You'll tackle open fields and woodland tracks as well as face precipitous slopes. The quad biking is run at weekends from March through to November in Hertfordshire. Minimum age for this session is 18.

Half Day 4×4 Off-Road Driving:
Three drivers and one instructor per off-road vehicle. With steep climbs and near vertical drops, these challenges will leave you totally exhilarated. Although this experience is shorter than the full day, you still get the thrills and spills of off-road driving. Run at weekends throughout the year in Welwyn, Herts. Minimum age 18.

Full Day 4×4 Off-Road Driving:
Three drivers and one instructor per vehicle. Take a swerve off the beaten track with a hair-raising off-road ride on a natural roller coaster. Run at weekends throughout the year in Welwyn, Herts. Minimum age 18.

Garlands Off Road & Corporate Leisure

Garlands Off Road & Corporate Leisure is based in the heart of the Midlands centrally located between Birmingham, Derby, Nottingham, Leicester and Coventry. Whether you are organising a stag or hen party or a corporate activity away day, our extensive venue, friendly service and quality activities make for an action-packed event whichever activities you choose!

Experiences:

- *Off-Road Karting.* Buckle up and prepare yourself to race our 400cc off-road karts around a dirt track. This fast-moving competitive activity is guaranteed to get the adrenalin flowing!
- *Quad Biking.* This time-trial racing activity is not for the faint hearted. Full tuition is provided on a one-to-one basis before participants are let loose on the racetrack to compete for the coveted Garlands medals
- *Archery.* Archery is a fun activity starting with one-to-one tuition then moving on to a competition
- *Clay Pigeon Shooting.* Under the guidance of our experienced instructors participants move around a variety of different stands and are given full tuition or simply advice and encouragement throughout
- *Laser Clay Pigeon Shooting.* This fast-moving competitive activity is ideal for groups of up to five participants shooting at the same clay at the same time!
- *4x4 Driving.* Test your driving abilities over rough terrain and obstacles including mud pits, embankments and logs, to name but a few!
- *Paintballing.* Paintballing combines teamwork, strategy and skill into an exciting activity for private groups and corporate entertainment alike

Activity Location:
Midlands

Contact Details:
Garlands Off Road & Corporate Leisure
T: 01827 722123
E: info@garlandsleisure.co.uk
W: www.garlandsleisure.co.uk

Practical Information:
Min. age 16 yrs for activities other than Clay Pigeon Shooting, 4x4 and Paintballing
Max. weight 18 stone for Quad Biking and Off-road Karting

Groups:
Min. of 8 people for Quad Biking, Off-road Karting and Laser Clay Pigeon Shooting
Min. of 4 people for Archery

Gift Vouchers:
Gift vouchers are available for all activities

Availability:
Open 7 days a week for all activities other than Clay Pigeon Shooting

Special Offer/Incentive:
The organiser goes free on any Quad Biking, Off-road Karting, Archery or Laser Clay Pigeon Shooting booking of 15 people or more.

Adrenaline

'There are only three sports, mountain climbing, bull fighting and motor racing, all the rest being games.'

ERNEST HEMINGWAY

Living on the edge

There's a saying amongst adventure sports people that 'if you're not living on the edge you're taking up too much space'. It's up to you to decide where that edge is, but when you've done so you should creep up to it and sneak a peek over the side. Whatever you do, don't forget to enjoy the ride while you're at it.

Adrenaline sports are all about having a go, not about being excluded because some smart marketing people have hijacked an activity, packaged it and sold it as a lifestyle for 'rad' dudes with tribal tattoos. The great thing about adventures like skydiving, mountain biking, paintballing or climbing is that pretty much anyone can have a go – and in the process decide for themselves just how far out their own particular 'edge' lies.

Skydiving, for example, is always going to be a good deal more scary than, say, scrabble, but just how full on it is depends on you.

Geronimo

In the past, the only way to skydive was to take a beginner's course and then jump solo. This is still the easiest way to get going on your own since the course will only take a day or two and consists of some straightforward drills for checking the 'chute, deploying the secondary 'chute if necessary, and rolling on landings to avoid injury. Then you're up and away for a fixed line jump which means that your 'chute cord is automatically pulled for you as you jump out of the plane.

There is an easier way to find out what it's like though – and that's the tandem jump. With a tandem jump you don't have to learn how to deploy your 'chute because you don't have to do anything of the kind. Besides, if you're in any doubt about what to do once out of the plane you can always ask the instructor since you will be strapped to him/her. With tandem you basically have an instructor strapped onto your back like a large and very reassuring rucksack. The instructor takes care of everything to do with getting you out of the plane and safely back to terra firma. All you have to do is scream.

Up against the wall

People have climbed for as long as they were bright enough to notice that some places were higher than others. No childhood is complete without at least one attempt to shin up a steep bank or hang off a tree, and rock climbing is a natural extension of that. If you've ever seen those vertigo-inducing pictures of climbers seemingly clinging like flies to sheer faces you'll know that it's an extension that can go a very long way towards the extreme. Yet while the adrenaline factor of climbing is unquestioned it is also a surprisingly cerebral sport in which the techniques are really about problem solving in three dimensions.

The obvious place to get started in sport climbing is on an artificial climbing wall. These have popped up all over the place and often take the form of fully equipped indoor climbing gyms. Artificial climbing walls come complete with overhangs, cracks and hand or footholds as well as bolts you can hook onto with your carabiners (the D-shaped clips which all climbers carry). Usually the grips are colour coded or numbered to give different routes up the wall, so that while you can use absolutely any point that comes to hand (or foot) in the beginning you can progress by restricting yourself to prescribed routes of varying difficulty.

The first thing to learn when getting the hang of a climbing wall is a technique called 'belaying', which gives you the reassurance of a safety rope leading from you, up to a point above you which acts as a pulley, and then back down to a partner who can keep you safe even if you were to get it into your head to throw yourself backwards off the wall.

Even letting go of the wall altogether means the climber won't fall but will dangle instead. Not elegant, maybe, but infinitely less painful than plummeting. So what are you waiting for?

All downhill from here

Mountain biking, like climbing, can be as adrenaline charged or as soothing as you wish. Anyone who can ride a bike can get out and about on big fat knobbly tires but the real trick to mountain biking is to remember that the hard bit isn't the going up – it's the coming back down. Mountain bike adventures are usually graded so you have a pretty good idea of what you're letting yourself in for, but if you really want to widen your eyes, blow your hair back and feel the rush then it's the descents that do it. Of course, you just might want to look for a course in handling a mountain bike over rough ground before you have a go. The weight distribution and reactions really aren't the same as they are back home – no matter how brave your bunny hops over kerbs.

Army Parachute Association

If you are a seasoned skydiver or someone contemplating their first jump, Netheravon is the place for you! Our skydiving club is run by the Army Parachute Association and we welcome military and civilian jumpers.

If you have never jumped before why don't you experience the thrill of a tandem skydive? For those of you who would prefer to go it alone we run static-line courses at weekends and have an AFF school which operates midweek as well as at weekends. If you are already hooked on skydiving then come along to the variety of events and competitions that run throughout the year.

Activity Location:
South West

Contact Details:
Army Parachute Association
T: 01980 678250
E: info@netheravon.com
W: www.netheravon.com

Practical Information:
Airfield camp is a military base. Please bring proof of identity with you
Canteen and bar on site

Availability:
Booking is recommended. Please call 01980 678250 for information

Special Offer:
A 10% discount is available to readers of *Ultimate Gift Experiences*. Cannot be combined with any other discount or promotional offer.

Experiences:

Static Line:
Considered to be the normal method of entry to the sport of parachuting, the student uses a parachute that is automatically opened once he/she has exited the aircraft.

Weekend course - ground-train on Saturday and jump on Sunday!

Courses run most weekends - booking is essential.

Tandem Parachuting:
This is the method of parachuting for those who want to experience the exhilaration of freefall parachuting but who do not want to progress any further within the sport. The student is free to enjoy the freefall descent from 12,500 feet whilst the instructor controls everything.

It is best to book at least three weeks in advance if you want to carry out a tandem descent.

Accelerated Freefall:
These courses are run by dedicated AFF instructors who will take the novice skydiver from Level 1 to Level 8, using the most up-to-date equipment and facilities available.

★ **10% DISCOUNT** Please mention *Ultimate Gift Experiences* when booking

British Parachute Schools

British Parachute Schools is the UK's biggest and busiest civilian skydiving centre (around 29,000 jumps a year), providing top-class training to thousands of new skydivers since 1977. We fly two fast 16-place turbine-powered Cessna Grand Caravan aircraft. Open seven days a week all year round with full-time professional staff always on hand to guide you. Central location, easy access from all parts of the country.

Activity Location:
Midlands

Contact Details:
British Parachute Schools Ltd
T: 01949 860878
E: info@bpslangar.co.uk
W: www.bpslangar.co.uk

Practical Information:
Min. age 16 (parents consent under 18). Doctor's certificate required 40 and over. Solo courses: maximum 102 kg and reasonable fitness required. Maximum 50 years. Tandem Skydives: maximum 95 kg, no upper age limit.

Special Offer/Incentive:
A 10% discount is available for readers of *Ultimate Gift Experiences*. Cannot be combined with any other discount or promotional offer.

★ **10% DISCOUNT** Please mention *Ultimate Gift Experiences* when booking

Experiences:

Tandem Skydive:
The wild ride – and the quick and easy way to skydive from 14,000 feet. Securely attached to a specially qualified instructor, you experience about a minute in freefall and five minutes under the parachute! Open to all; many less able participants welcome.

Basic Skydiving Course:
Two-day course culminating in your first jump from 3,500 feet using an automatically opened modern high-performance parachute. Great fun for groups – and a great sense of achievement. Your first step to becoming a qualified skydiver!

Accelerated Freefall:
Our intensive course, skydiving from 14,000 feet with two instructors who coach you while you fall. A full day's ground training prepares you for this eight-jump package. The quickest way to take up skydiving as your sport! Or just take the first jump to see how you like it!

Clive Powell Mountain Bikes

Clive Powell Mountain Bikes are a small family business running fully packaged mountain bike weekends in mid-Wales.

Activity Location:
Wales

Contact Details:
Clive Powell Mountain Bikes
T: 01597 811343
E: clive@clivepowell-mtb.co.uk
W: www.clivepowell-mtb.co.uk

Practical Information:
All our weekends feature great riding with myself and my hand picked team of guides. Routes are chosen considerately to suit the abilities of all riders in the group
Short cuts and extra loops are usually built into the ride. If the group size is large, or of a very mixed ability, there will be more than one guide.

Availability:
Selected weekends throughout the year. Please see www.clivepowell-mtb.co.uk for more information or telephone 01597 811343

Experiences:

Dirty Weekends:
Clive Powell's Dirty Weekends are fully packaged mountain bike (and now also road bike) weekends. Complete with accommodation, food, guiding and support. Dirty Weekends are based in Rhayader near the Elan Valley in mid-Wales, an area renowned for its spectacular dams and reservoirs. Rhayader is surrounded by open hills with some of the best mountain biking terrain in Britain. We have weekends suitable for everyone from novice to expert.

We are situated midway between Snowdonia National Park and the Brecon Beacons National Park.

- Superb mountain biking terrain over open hills and spectacular unspoilt scenery
- Experienced, qualified guide
- Support vehicle to bring out picnic lunches, spares and tools
- Real home cooking
- Friendly atmosphere

Spy Games

Spy Games have taken the best action and adventure from the world of secret agents and designed a range of events and activities that allow anyone to experience for themselves.

From individuals to large corporate groups, we are the only specialist provider of spy events and experiences because no one else has the activities, equipment and expertise that we have.

Activity Locations:
North West, Midlands and South East

Contact Details:
Spy Games Ltd
T: 0845 1303 007
E: info@spy-games.com
W: www.spy-games.com

Practical Information:
Our gift experiences are suitable for people of any age over 17 (with a full driving license for the full day, parents/legal guardians required for under 18s)

Equipment:
We provide all the necessary equipment for the activities, together with an excellent buffet lunch on the full day event. Spectators are welcome

Vouchers:
Gift vouchers available

Special Offers:
A 10% discount is available for readers of *Ultimate Gift Experiences*. Cannot be combined with any other discount or promotional offer.

★ **10% DISCOUNT** Please mention *Ultimate Gift Experiences* when booking

Experiences:

Spy Academy:
Learn some essential skills required to conduct a secret agent operation, how to use specialist spy equipment like covert cameras and UHF radios, bugs and listening devices and lock picking gadgets. You'll be taught how to use a pistol, the secret agent's personal weapon, and then test your skills with quick-draw techniques in a VIP protection scenario.

You'll fire machine guns on our Close Quarter Battle area, apply precision shooting through the powerful telescopic sight of our sniper rifles, try your skill at axe throwing, and test your nerve and concentration with our bomb deactivation challenge. Also, our hi-tech laser combat system is used in a harmless shoot-out to practice 'contact drills'.

You'll also receive some expert instruction on unarmed combat techniques, useful when you're cornered by enemy agents!

Spy Games Gift Experience:
This is the full-on secret agent business, where you get to do all of the Spy Academy activities, and then the action moves onto driving skills. This is genuine evasive driving instruction and you'll be shown how to manoeuvre and control the car Spy Games style – and we wear out a lot of tyres! You're behind the wheel and carrying out J-turns, handbrake turns, and anti-ambush drills.

Then there's the drive-in shooting range – skid to a halt, shoot the targets from the car and then speed off again against the clock.

The UK Bungee Club

We are the largest bungee club in the UK offering nationwide locations along with the worlds only indoor bungee site, The Abyss. The club was established in 1992 and we have successfully jumped over 100,000 people safely, helping raise in excess of £1,000,000 for good causes. Insured by Lloyds of London for £5m.

Activity Location:
Nationwide

Contact Details:
The UK Bungee Club
T: 07000 286433
E: enquiries@ukbungee.co.uk
W: www.ukbungee.co.uk

Practical information:
Strict medical restrictions apply
No under 14s
14 and 15-year-olds require parental or guardian permission.

Availability:
Various throughout the UK, check our website for full listings. www.ukbungee.co.uk

Special Offer/Incentive:
For group bookings of ten or more we offer a 10% discount.

Experiences:

Indoor Bungee:

Take a leap into The Abyss @ Magna. It's the UK's scariest adrenaline experience, the worlds only indoor bungee jump and the only permanent bungee jumping facility in the UK.

Picture the scene: you are enveloped in semi-darkness, spotlights whirl around Magna's breathtaking structure, the Face of Steel, standing at 150 feet; you start the 143-step climb to the jump zone, music pumping, dry ice fills the air and 7 huge video screens project images of what you are about to experience ... That's before you've even taken the plunge!

Outdoor Bungee:

We have four mobile operations that facilitate over 120 different jump dates and places across the UK.

Mobile rigs – *the facts for bungee jumping and catapulting*

- Height: 170ft (Nelson's column, 160ft; Statue of Liberty 302ft)
- Cord and backup: 8-metre rubber cord, stretched to three times its length, plus static line
- Drop speed: 0–60 takes 1.9 secs
- G-Force: Jumpers experience 2g

★ 10% DISCOUNT
For group bookings of ten or more

Hydro Extreme Action Sports

Try something new, something that provides action, excitement, adventure and new challenges. Traction and Power Kites are high performance wings capable of generating a tremendous amount of power. The combination of skills needed to fly these hi-spec kites and the exhilarating experience of riding your kite buggy to speeds of 60 mph is the reason why so many become addicted to power kiting.

Activity Location:
Midlands

Contact Details:
Hydro Extreme Action Sports Park
T: 01905 620044
E: info@hydroextreme.com
W: www.hydroextreme.com

Practical Information:
If clients are unable to swim 25 metres, the chief instructor must be notified prior to the course
Anyone suffering from any medical conditions must notify Hydro Extreme prior to booking and again on arrival at the centre. The company can accept no responsibility for any client's medical condition

Availability:
All courses or personal coaching are available 7 days a week. Please phone 01905 620044 for more details.

Experiences:

Power Kiting and Kite Buggying:
During the first half of the course we will teach you how to control the power kites and the basic flying techniques. The second half will focus on buggying. You will experience the thrill of piloting your buggy powered by wind alone; we will take you through getting going across the wind, tracking upwind, downwind and linking it all together with turns – and of course stopping!

Power Kiting and Landboarding:
As above but the second half of the course will focus on landboarding. The new kid on the block of power kiting using the recently developed 4-wheeled All Terrain Boards with the addition of high-performance traction foil kites. All the kite surf tricks are possible like back loops, front loops, grabs and board offs – and a whole lot more!

Kitesurfing:
One of the fastest growing water sports today, combining skills from windsurfing, wakeboarding and power kiting. It is an easy sport to learn but you will soon be hooked on the speed and the massive jumps only possible over water.

Maxtrack

Maxtrack has been in the mountainboard business since day one. They were the first people to start mountainboarding in the UK back in 1997, and never looked back. Now Maxtrack design and construct mountainboard centres all over Europe and specialise in MBS Mountainboards –the market leaders.

Experiences:

Mountainboarding is the fastest-growing land sport in the UK. The feeling of carving down a hillside is similar to snowboarding, but unlike snowboarding can be done all year round.

Mountainboard centres offer a safe and fun environment for those looking for their next adrenaline rush.

Taster Course (2hrs):

Learn to tackle your first carves and power slides safely with the aid of a fully qualified instructor at any one of the recognised centres throughout the UK.

Using top equipment from top brands, and all the safety equipment, you'll find yourself flying down the hill with confidence and ease.

'The Mountainboard Experience' – half day (4hrs)

Learn safely and then master your skills. A fully qualified instructor will guide you through your first carves and get you up and running confidently. He/she will then be on hand to guide you off the beginner slope and on to more challenging parts of the centre should you wish to tackle these. Rails, jumps and boardercross tracks will all be there and waiting to offer you an adrenaline rush like nothing else.

Activity Location:
Nationwide

Contact Details:
Maxtrack
T: 0870 242 7626
E: info@maxtrack.com
W: www.maxtrack.com

Practical Information:
Minimum age 7 years

Equipment:
All equipment will be provided, including safety pads

Recommended:
Old clothes to ride in/spare change of clothes
Sturdy trainers/ankle boots

Availability:
Weekends and selected weekdays

Corporate bookings:
Any of the above activities can be tailored to your needs

Special Offer/Incentive:
You'll get a 10% discount when you quote REF: Directex2006SP. Cannot be combined with any other discount or promotional offer.

★ 10% DISCOUNT
When you quote REF: Directex2006SP

Airkix

and what we do ...

Imagine a wind tunnel that could be used for testing the aerodynamics of an F1 racing car, turn it upright, step into the airflow and you are skydiving. It's a proven concept operating in several countries to the benefit of the skydiving community and anyone else who wishes to taste the thrill of freefall in a completely safe environment.

Activity Location:
South East

Contact Details:
Airkix
T: 0845 331 6549
E: info@airkix.com
W: www.airkix.com

Practical Information:
Wind tunnel flying is for anyone of reasonable fitness. If you have a physical disability please call us prior to booking

Equipment:
Free gear hire – we supply everything you need to fly!

Opening Days:
Open 7 days a week including bank holidays. Please ring to check times and availability

Special Offer/Incentive:
Discounts available for off-peak, repeat flyers and group bookings.

Experiences:

Airkix packages involve a one-hour experience including the following:

Kix-start:

- A fun briefing and instruction period, in which you will learn and practice free-fall and bodyflying techniques
- Free locker hire
- Free gear hire – everything you need to fly ... we supply!
- Two flights of one minute each – that's the same free-fall time as three tandem skydives
- A personalised flight certificate for each flyer

Air-born:

- As above but includes two flights of two minutes each – that's the same free-fall time as six tandem skydives

Learn to Fly:

- As Kix-start and Air-born but with five flights of two minutes each – after which we aim to have given you the free-fall skills equivalent to, if not better than, a newly qualified skydiver!

SphereMania

The ultimate white-knuckle experience!

The idea of being pushed down a hill inside a massive inflatable Sphere may seem crazy to some, but we guarantee you the most unique ride of your life at one of our official SphereMania UK locations.

Climb inside our spherical world and enjoy the thrill and exhilaration of 'Sphereing' with SphereMania!

Experiences:

Sphereing

The thrill and unique experience you'll get from 'Sphereing' at one of our many UK sites can be enjoyed by people of many ages.

Rolling down a hill inside the Sphere at speeds of up to 30mph is a pure adrenaline rush! You may have already tried bungee jumping or other extreme sports, but the exhilaration and feeling you'll get from 'Sphereing' will leave you wanting to roll again and again!

Aqua Sphereing

Have you ever wondered what it's like to be inside a washing machine whilst it's on? Well now you can find out at one of our official SphereMania UK locations.

With no harnesses to stop you slipping and sliding around inside the Sphere, we challenge you to enjoy the sensations of a huge aqua experience. You will be sliding inside the Aqua Sphere along with twenty litres of water. Prepare to get wet and feel the rush of Aqua Sphereing!

Why visit SphereMania?

SphereMania offers you a truly unique, exhilarating and totally radical experience, completely different from other adventure sports.

Face up to the ultimate challenge and experience the ride of your life!

Activity Location:
Nationwide
We are constantly opening new SphereMania sites, so please visit our website www.spheremania.com for the most up-to-date list of venues

Contact Details:
SphereMania
T: 07932 99 66 20
E: info@spheremania.com
W: www.spheremania.com

Practical Information:
Not suitable for anyone under 1.5 m height for Harness Sphereing and 1m for Aqua Sphereing
Fully safety accredited by ADIPS (Amusement Device Inspection Permit Scheme)
All operators are fully trained to ensure your safety and enjoyment

Equipment:
All equipment and safety harnesses provided (for Harness Sphereing)
Customers need to wear long-sleeved t-shirt and comfortable trousers
Please bring a change of clothes and towel if Aqua Sphereing

Vouchers:
Gift vouchers available at www.spheremania.com

Availability:
Sites usually operate between Easter and September

Special Offer/Incentive:
Special offers available to readers of *Ultimate Gift Experiences* – please call for details.

Activity Location:
Scotland

Contact Details:
The Ice Factor
T: 01855 831100
E: info@ice-factor.co.uk
W: www.ice-factor.co.uk

Equipment:
Full instruction and equipment available

Availability:
Open 7 days a week
The centre can be extremely busy during weekends and holiday periods so advance booking by telephone is always advisable

Special Offer/Incentive:
Book midweek (excluding holiday periods) to receive a 15% discount
Book 3 places get 1 place half price
Book 4 places get 1 place free
Quote DE/IFL/JS

★ **15% DISCOUNT** (see above)

The Ice Factor

The Ice Factor is the UK's premier mountain activity centre. Home to the world's biggest indoor ice climbing facility and the UK's highest articulated rock climbing wall, the facility is a must-visit location for adventurers and thrill seekers of all ages.

The centre is located between Ben Nevis and Glencoe mountain ranges and does more climbing instruction than every other facility in Britain, put together!

Experiences:

Hit the Ice:
This is a 3-hour course where you will be taught how to use crampons and ice axes (supplied) as you scale the world's biggest indoor ice wall. Throughout you will be under the supervision of a qualified mountaineering instructor. The ultimate chill!

Taste the Rock:
This is a 1½-hour introduction to rock climbing. You will learn how to tackle overhangs, gullies and steep crack systems. Your instructor will coach you on abseiling as you lower off from 50ft above the ground. A must for the adrenaline junky!

There is a range of indoor and outdoor activities including Ice Climbing, Rock Climbing, Kid's Club, Coffee Shop, Licensed Bar Bistro, Sauna & Steam Rooms and an outdoor shop selling a full range of equipment and gifts.

Firefighter Experience

Can you imagine how exciting it is to ride in a fire engine with lights and sirens on? The adrenaline rush you get when you arrive at the scene to a blazing inferno? *You no longer have to imagine ... experience the excitement!*

Experiences:

Join the Fire Service
Most brigades only recruit every 12–18 months and can get up to 300 applicants for each job. This course is a unique opportunity to go right through the selection process in a single weekend. We show you how to increase your chance of selection.

Firefighter Experience
This is a two-hour adult package where you dress in fire kit, ride in a fire engine and fight real fires.

Family Firefighter Experience
This is a great opportunity for parents to participate and bond with their children in a fun and exciting way. Fill the fire engine with water and learn a fire drill. Then get turned out on a shout! Minimum age 5 years.

Hen/Stag Parties
We have great half day or full days of firefighting fun waiting for you. We can even arrange other activities locally for those wanting a full and varied day.

Fire Engine Limo
Need a fire engine limo in North Lancs/South Cumbria? We're the guys!

Activity Location:
North West

Contact Details:
Firefighter Experience
T: 01539 56 42 42
E: info@firefighterexperience.com
W: www.firefighterexperience.com

Practical information:
Wear lightweight clothing or shorts. You get hot in fire kit! Children's clothing – lightweight suits supplied. Please bring change of clothes/ wellingtons

Instructors:
All our instructors are either serving or retired firefighters

Availability:
All events need to be pre-booked. Open throughout the year

Gift vouchers:
We can supply gift vouchers for all our experiences

Special Offer/Incentive:
Special discounts available to readers of *Ultimate Gift Experiences* – please call for details.

TYF Adventure

Great outdoor adventure in Pembrokeshire's best landscapes. We have a fantastic adventure and learning program which includes day and residential courses, designed to engage, inspire and excite.

Activity location:
Wales

Contact Details:
TYF Adventure
T: 01437 721611
E: info@tyf.com
W: www.tyf.com

Equipment:
All training and safety equipment is provided

Availability:
Throughout the year

Groups:
We can accommodate in excess of 100 people

Experiences:

Fantastic adventure and learning programmes to suit everyone.

Coasteering:
This is the activity that TYF are justly famous for – exciting, energetic, sometimes scary and never to be forgotten. Scrambling over rocks, jumping from cliffs, swimming in the sea, washed by waves ... this is coasteering. An outdoor adventure pursuit that can push your adrenaline levels or simply unwind you.

Coasteering is top of the bill but don't miss out on the rest including:

- Surfing
- Rock Climbing
- Kayaking
- Canoeing

Short Break Adventure:
TYF's short breaks come in all sizes with all sorts of events. The No Limits & Spirit of Adventure weekends are ideal to have a go at a mix of adventures or you may be looking to learn the ropes with our sea kayaking, surfing and climbing courses. Our calendar has our fixed-date courses, but don't let that limit your options; any short break is available year round for groups of four or more people.

Airbossworld

Powerkiting has been around for over 30 years, and in that time the sport has progressed unbelievably. We have watched the sport evolve. There is no other sport that gives you such an adrenaline rush as Powerkiting.

Airbossworld started tuition in 2000. Between us we hold over 40 years of flying experience. Tuition ranges from basic to advanced riders and all of our staff are IKO qualified.

Experiences:

Powerkite Taster Course:
After some safety instructions you will be let loose for an hour of blasting around with the latest kites the sport has to offer. Duration: 1 hour.

Basic Course:
Never flown a kite before? Then this is the course for you – teaching the very basics of flying four line kites, with control tips and safety points. The end of the day sees you having total control of the kite in all conditions and situations from unpacking to packing down. Duration: 10am–4pm.

Buggy/Board Course:
We concentrate on getting you going on wheels in either the buggy or board. Duration: 10am–4pm.

One 2 One Course:
This is for those of you that want to fine-tune your technique, gain confidence after a wipe out, or find out why something is not quite going right. This gives you the opportunity to tell the instructor what you want to brush up on with extra tips and feedback. Duration: 3 hours (am or pm).

Team Building, Stag and Hen Parties:
Taste the power of the wind and watch your mates get big air! Up to 12 in a party. Duration: 3 hours (am or pm).

Activity Location:
Midlands

Contact Details:
Airbossworld
T: 01509 852693/07773 266548
E: gary@airbossworld.co.uk
W: www.airbossworld.co.uk

Practical Information:
Minimum age 8 years
Items to remember on the day: water, sunglasses, clothes to suit the weather conditions, supportive shoes
If on an all day course bring some lunch
Limited refreshments available on site

Availability:
Pre-booking essential. Via the website www.airbossworld.co.uk or by telephone 01509 852693

Special Offer/Incentive:
Please mention that you found our details in *Ultimate Gift Experiences* to qualify for a 10% discount. Cannot be combined with any other discounts or promotional offers.

★ **10% DISCOUNT** Please mention *Ultimate Gift Experiences* when booking

Animal adventures

'A horse is dangerous at both ends and uncomfortable in the middle.'

IAN FLEMING

Wet and wild

The great outdoors wouldn't have half the appeal if it wasn't for the things that live in it – and we all know how even a simple walk in the country becomes magical if you cross the path of a badger or deer.

So imagine how much more thrilling it is to get up close and personal with the more elusive creatures. You don't have to go on safari to the Serengeti to feel the thrill of an encounter with wildlife. You can do it right here in the British Isles.

Whale of a tale

A friend of mine was once sneezed on by a whale. He ended up pretty much covered head to foot in blowhole-blasted mucus and while he didn't go so far as to say it was pleasant he admitted that it was about the only time in his whole life he could say he felt honoured to be decorated that way.

Marine mammals have a power to captivate and enthral precisely because they are of this world and yet not of it. The appealing faces of seals, the questing eyes of whales and the famous dolphin smile are in stark contrast to their otherwise fishy appearance and their acrobatic litheness in the waves. Close up with the seals it becomes very easy to understand the Celtic selkie myths of seals that can shed their skins and walk as humans. Nobody who has seen dolphins leaping in the bow wave of a boat will ever forget it; and as for whales, endangered behemoths of the deep, just glimpsing one is the experience of a lifetime.

You don't have to go to sea to experience the wild up close. Falconry courses are a great way of seeing aerial predators. In fact, falconry is about the only way you are going to come face to face with those graceful hawks, eagles, and giant eagle owls – the kind of creatures normally only seen as specks through binoculars. Take up the gauntlet of a falconry experience and you will get to 'fly' the birds yourself, getting to know them, their habits and manners, and of course, feeling the thrill of an eagle on your arm.

Let someone else do the legwork

It's a fact long exploited by hunters that animals are less unnerved by humans on horseback than humans on their own two legs. Anything that lets you get close up to the wilderness is great by me especially if I can also get someone else to do all the legwork. Which only seems right if that someone happens to be generously gifted in the legs department.

Speaking as a city slicker with a healthy respect for big hairy things with teeth, I was surprised to find that horse trekking is, by and large, amazingly easy and laid-back. Find yourself a reputable establishment with healthy-looking horses and you are in for one of those outdoor activities (like sailing) that leaves you satisfyingly tired and hungry – only without having done any work.

There are a few tips to ponder before leaping into the saddle and shouting 'Yippee Kay-ay!'

- Leading the horse is best done by walking level with its head and turning it by leading it around the outside of you – don't try turning by walking across its front or you'll end up pushing against half a ton of horse while trying to avoid the hooves
- Going through a gate means leading the horse all the way through, probably turning it around so that you are able to shut the gate again. Don't expect the horse to make room for your legs as you go through together
- As you mount the horse make sure you have the reins in your hand but not held so tightly that you pull the horse's head back as you swing onto the saddle. Failing to hold the reins means that your horse is very likely to wander off just as you are trying to get up – cue hilarity all round
- Keep the reins in your hands, which should be centred in front and low. Don't have too much slack otherwise, when it comes time to rein in, you'll have to pull right back which will shift your own weight backwards and destabilise you
- Nudging the horse (you shouldn't have to kick it) takes it up a gear and doing it again takes it up another gear, though for much trekking a walk is the fastest speed you will have to worry about

Catanger Llamas

Personally guided treks whilst you enjoy the beautiful Northamptonshire countryside leading one of our gentle llamas along bridleways, farm tracks and country lanes.

All treks start with a general introduction to llamas, followed by instruction on handling them and meeting the llamas themselves.

Activity Location:
Midlands

Contact Details:
Mary Pryse
Catanger Llamas
T: 01295 768676
E: mary@llamatrekking.co.uk
W: llamatrekking.co.uk

Availability:
Open all year round. Booking essential

Gift Vouchers:
Available for half-day and full-day treks

Practical Information:
Disabled access is limited; please contact us for advice
Single trekkers are welcome subject to booking dates

Special Offer/Incentive:
Children 8–12 years free of charge but must be accompanied by one adult for each child for half-day and picnic treks.

Experiences:

- *Half Day Experience.* We trek across country through arable, pasture and woodland. The trek covers 4–4 ½ miles and takes around 2 hours. Back at the farm you are invited to visit our mothers and babies and to see what we make from our llama fibre. You are welcome to picnic on the farm before or after your trek or you can sample one of the local country inns. This trek is available all year round
- *Picnic Trek.* We travel further across country, all off-road. After about 2 hours we stop for a home-prepared picnic lunch and rest for an hour or so whilst the llamas do likewise. The trek back to Catanger takes just under an hour and on our return we visit the mothers and babies followed by tea and cake in the llama lodge. The distance covered is around 6.5 miles. Lunch and all refreshments are included. Available April–October
- *Special 'On-farm' Treks.* Lasting just an hour and walking through specially mown rides in our 20 acre wood at Catanger, these treks are for those who cannot manage the 4 mile treks across country. You are then welcome to visit the mothers and babies and to picnic on the farm. Not suitable for children under seven years. Available on selected days all year round. No vouchers
- *Corporate and Private Party Trekking.* Corporate entertaining, large family groups, charity fundraising events, team-building adventure groups, clubs, schools and children's parties. Groups from 6 to 30 people

Hyde Park Riding School Ltd

Hyde Park Stables offer riding all year round on horses and ponies chosen for their safe temperament. There are five miles of bridleways for riding around Hyde Park in Central London, including Rotton Row, the most famous venue for riding for the past 300 years. There are also two outdoor riding arenas for more formal lessons, including dressage.

Location:
Central London

Contact Details:
Hyde Park Stables
T: 020 7723 2813
E: info@hydeparkstables.com
W: www.hydeparkstables.com

Practical Information:
Age limit six years and upward, maximum weight 12.5 stone/75 kg

Equipment:
Hats and boots provided free of charge

Availability:
Open 7 days a week from 7:30am to 5pm

Gift Vouchers:
Gift Vouchers available for all rides, lessons and courses

Special Offer/Incentive:
A 10% discount is available on children's courses of 10 hours
A 15% discount is available on adults' courses of 10 hours

Experiences:

The stables cater for riders of all abilities, both adults and children, in groups, private rides and riding lessons. Beginners are very welcome and previous experience is not necessary. Groups catered for and intensive courses available for staff incentives and team building.

The stables offer a high standard of teaching, with friendly, efficient staff.

- Ride in London's famous Hyde Park
- All rides accompanied by instructors/escorts
- See some of London's most famous landmarks on horseback including the Diana Memorial Fountain, Albert Memorial, Queen Elizabeth Gate, Speakers Corner and Serpentine Lake

★ **10% DISCOUNT**
on children's courses of 10 hours

★ **15% DISCOUNT**
on adults' courses of 10 hours

The Marine Connection

The Marine Connection is a London-based charity specifically set up for the protection and conservation of dolphins and whales. One of the charity's main aims is to ensure as many people as possible realise and understand about the importance of protecting these marine mammals and their natural habitat. One way the charity achieves this is through campaigning, education and research.

Experiences:

UK Dolphin and Whale Watching Trips:

The Marine Connection organises boat trips around the British Isles, in association with qualified skippers who follow strict Codes of Conduct to protect the wildlife we encounter. Operating in Cornwall, Scotland and Wales we offer the general public a unique opportunity to see dolphins and whales in their natural environment. Species sighted include bottlenose, common and Risso's dolphins, and basking sharks. Throughout the winter months there is also the opportunity to see some of the larger whales including fin and minke. Money raised from these trips supports the charity's vital research work on the marine mammals that frequent these areas and also other Marine Connection projects and campaigns worldwide.

Activity Location:
South West, Wales and Scotland

Contact Details:
The Marine Connection
T: 020 7499 9196
E: info@marineconnection.org
W: www.marineconnection.org

Practical Information:
Cornwall: year round
Trips depart from Falmouth with complimentary car parking for Marine Connection passengers. The boat carries a maximum of twelve and is fitted with a hydrophone to enable you to hear the dolphins underwater. The Cornwall trips include the use of thermal suits. Minimum age is six. Each trip lasts 2 hours

Scotland: April–October
Trips depart from Buckie in the Moray Firth. The boat carries a maximum of twelve. There are complimentary binoculars provided onboard for your use. Minimum age is six. These trips last for 2½ hours and include complimentary drinks

Wales: April–October
Trips depart from New Quay. The boat carries a maximum of twelve and is fitted with a hydrophone to enable you to hear the dolphins underwater. As with all our trips, there is full commentary and interaction between crew and passengers with opportunities for relaxed photography. Minimum age is six. Each trip lasts 2 hours

Warwick International School of Riding

The school is run as a family business and qualified instructors have the experience to provide caring and professional assistance and tuition. Set in the heart of Shakespeare's County, close to Warwick Castle, Warwick School of Riding can provide a range of individual and group activities for all age groups and abilities.

Activity Location:
Midlands

Contact details:
Warwick International School of Riding
T: 01926 494313
E: info.warwickriding.co.uk
W: www.warwickriding.co.uk

Additional Information:
Riding clothes to be worn if possible. If not, trousers, waterproofs and boots with small flat heel – no trainers
All riders must wear an approved riding hat. Riding hats will be supplied, although the School prefers the customer to use their own fitted hat

Special Offers:
A 10% discount is available on full day Fun Riding – please quote DE/WSR when booking. Not to be combined with any other offer, discount or promotion.

Experiences:

- *Lessons.* Can be taken with groups or on an individual basis. Weekly and weekend lessons available
- *Fun Days.* A full day at the centre for adults and children. Fun all-day riding (lunch not included), rosettes to win! Any ability welcome. Children supervised at all times. Learn how to prepare the horses including grooming and tacking up
- *Hacking.* The 2-hour hack is the most popular, incorporating a few optional natural obstacles and a lovely stream for riding in. All the horses are excellent and well behaved on the roads. A 3-hour hack can get you to Kenilworth Castle, lovely on a summer's day, and longer hacks can be organised with pub stops
- *Show Jumping.* Situated on one of the three all-weather sand ménages, which is also available for hire. The show jumping area is regularly used in lessons to encourage variety. Clear Round jumping classes available
- *Cross Country.* Course of 35 jumps. Lessons are available on the course. Regular competitions take place on the course for experienced riders and advanced riders
- *The Gallops.* All weather sand one mile track. Safe and well maintained, they can be used to blow the cobwebs away. Great for exercise, ideal when the weather is bad, or just enjoy a full gallop! Gallops available to hire throughout the year

★ **10% DISCOUNT** on full day Fun Riding – please quote DE/WSR when booking

The Knights of Middle England

With over ten years of jousting experience in live shows and displays, The Knights of Middle England are a radical newborn medieval jousting team that are bringing the 'Knights of Old' into the 21st century! We are based in the heart of Warwickshire, neighbouring the famous Warwick Castle. A perfect setting for our jousting team to teach you how to joust!

Our aim is to provide unique entertainment within the medieval era of this traditional sport.

Activity Location:
Midlands

Contact details:
The Knights of Middle England
T: 01926 400401
E: info@knightsofmiddleengland.co.uk
W: www.knightsofmiddleengland.co.uk

Additional Information:
All armour and charger is provided
Sensible footwear (flat sole, small heel) and a change of clothes, as you must be prepared to get muddy
A reasonable level of fitness is required
Riding ability not essential

Special Offers:
Discount of £10 per person available to readers. Please quote DE/KME when booking. Cannot be combined with any other offer, discount or promotion.

Experiences:

- *Spectacular Jousting Shows.* Actors, stuntmen and performers supply a show to remember with the pageantry, honour and chivalry from this colourful middle age
- *Activity Days:* learn how to joust at Knight School. These exciting days are carried out on a very basic level with safety being foremost. Riding experience is an advantage but not essential. Basic jousting skills are taught, learn how to use a lance and shield, strike the quintaine, and authentic mounted skill at arms games. You will have the chance to dress up in full medieval costume, have your own title and coat of arms and the day culminates with a contact joust against an instructor
- *Corporate Team Building.* Based around the Activity Day theme, with team tasks to be completed, knights are split into teams and battle it out with lance shield and sword to see which one of them can end the final quest of the Gauntlet Challenge and win the title of 'Sir Lancelot of the Day'
- *Private Events/Lessons & Courses.* Training is offered on a group, private, full day or weekend basis. We also provide entertainment for private events. For example:
    - Marriage Proposal – be a true knight in shining armour, with full medieval costume and steed. Brides parade to the church on horseback accompanied by knights. Propose in that unique way
    - Stag & Hen parties – an unforgettable time for that important event. A full day or weekend, packages can include hog roast and accommodation

From our base in the Midlands, the team can travel to your function or you can join us in the heart of Warwickshire.

★ **£10 DISCOUNT**
When you quote REF: DE/KME

J.R.C.S Falconry

J.R.C.S Falconry has a private collection of over 20 birds. From the beautiful barn owl and the hunting hawk to the feisty falcon and canny kestrel, there's sure to be a bird for everyone, young or old!

Set up in 2001, J.R.C.S. Falconry is based near Rugby in Warwickshire. It is ideally situated close to some beautiful flying countryside and within easy reach of the motorway networks.

Activity Location:
Midlands

Contact Details:
JRCS Falconry
T: 01788 890096/07736 524 512
E: jan@jrcsfalconry.co.uk
W: www.jrcsfalconry.co.uk

Practical Information:
At all times, whilst with any of the birds, you are accompanied by an experienced and qualified falconer, for your safety as well as that of the birds. The birds' welfare is always first and foremost in our minds

Availability:
Please telephone for course details and booking information

Special Offers:
A 10% discount is available for readers of *Ultimate Gift Experiences*. Cannot be combined with any other discount or promotional offer.

Experiences:

Birds of Prey Experience Days:
These are for bird enthusiasts who would like to come along and spend a day learning more about these wonderful creatures. Start the day with coffee/tea and a short introduction to the laws relating to birds of prey; then move on to the safety aspects of handling the birds and the equipment needed for falconry. Then you're ready to meet the hawks, falcons and owls and to see them fly. Finally, it's your turn to be really involved with and excited by these majestic birds, as you take your chance to handle and fly them for yourself.

Falconry Courses:
Our falconry courses run over three or five days. Courses can be tailored for students wishing to fully embrace the true art of falconry. We also provide refresher courses for falconers who want to bring themselves up to date with the latest in falconry.

★ **10% DISCOUNT** Please mention *Ultimate Gift Experiences* when booking

Bob Hogg Sheepdogs

Bob Hogg is a member of the International Sheepdog Society who travels throughout the country with his team of working sheepdogs. He has earned himself an excellent reputation for his professional and highly entertaining displays in which the dogs work sheep, geese and ducks. Bob has appeared on television many times including recently *The House of Tiny Tearaways* and ITV's *Date My Daughter*.

Activity Location:
Nationwide

Contact Details:
Bob Hogg
T: 01993 773849/07711 887161
E: bob.hogg1@btinternet.com
W: www.bobhoggsheepdogs.co.uk

Availability:
Selected weekdays and weekends throughout the year

Experiences:

Hands On:
Many people will have watched programmes such as BBC's *One Man and His Dog* and marvelled at the skill and understanding between man and dog.

You may have a sheepdog of your own and have always wondered if it had a working instinct. Or you may have a dog that needs that little bit of extra training.

We can offer a unique opportunity to learn for yourself how a sheepdog is trained, from a young pup to a fully trained top class worker, and provide a hands-on opportunity to work a sheepdog yourself under Bobs expert tuition. You will be able to gather sheep, learn the commands and whistles that will make a truly thrilling and rewarding experience.

Sheepdog Displays:
The display is both informative for adults and great fun for the children as they are invited into the arena whilst the dogs work the ducks around an obstacle course.

Corporate/Fun Days:
Very popular in the corporate market where clients are invited to go duck or geese herding. Informative and hilarious, the idea is to work as a team. Will things go according to plan or will the ducks get their revenge? I think so.

Previous clients include Everyman Motor Racing, Newbury Races, ITV, BBC and MTV Europe.

Burley Villa School of Riding

Whether you are a beginner or a seasoned rider, young or old, we can take you horse riding in 94,000 acres of ancient New Forest woodlands. There is no better way to enjoy the forest. Beginners always welcome.

Burley Villa is British Horse Society approved. We are proud of the standard we offer and of our horses and facilities.

Activity Location:
South West

Contact Details:
Burley Villa School of Riding
T: 01425 610728
E: burleyv@globalnet.co.uk
W: www.burleyvilla.co.uk

Practical Information:
Riding Lessons – min age 4 years
Forest Hacking – min age 7 years
Hard hats and Stetsons are provided
Weight limits apply on all lessons (14 st) and Hacks (15 st)

Availability:
Booking is essential

Special Offer/Incentive:
A 10% discount is available to readers. Please mention Direct Experiences when booking. Cannot be combined with any other special offer, discount or promotion.

★ **10% DISCOUNT** Please mention Direct Experiences when booking

Experiences:

English Riding:
Burley Villa welcomes both riders and non riders to ride out through the forest or for lessons in the arena. Forest Hacks are based on the rider's ability, with walk rides for beginners and walk & trot hacks for more experienced riders. Lessons are available for anyone from four years of age upwards. Try 'An Introduction to Riding' with a beginner lesson, forest hack and barbecue lunch.

Western Riding:
You don't have to be John Wayne to trail ride, most of our riders have never been on horses before, so there is no excuse... get your jeans on and ride the range!

Two hour trails leave throughout the day to just meander the forest on beautiful horses in a wonderful setting and, on our sundowner BBQ trail, enjoy the beauty of the forest as the sun sets, then riding back to a sizzling 'steak n chicken' barbecue around the campfire. For the youngsters try 'A Cowboy Adventure for Kids'.

Riding Breaks:
Come and stay in the New Forest. Sample the peace of country life and the beautiful forest from horseback.

Driving

'O bliss! O poop poop! O my! O my!'

MR TOAD, THE WIND IN THE WILLOWS, ON SEEING HIS FIRST SHINY MOTOR CAR

Wheelspins

'Understeer'. I think he was saying 'understeer'. Actually he might as well have been saying 'kumquaat' because all reasonable conversation was being stymied by a noise like a teenager doing handbrake turns in a Boeing 747.

I tried to lip-read but it's surprisingly hard when the person you're communicating with has gritted teeth, cheeks pulled back to somewhere around his ears and hands exerting a Vulcan death grip on the dashboard.

My first track session was a blast. Well it was for me. The instructor didn't seem quite so happy. He had spent some time talking about perfect lines through corners and the like only for this particular yahoo to spend the next twenty minutes destroying tyres and snaking all over the place. Which is not, incidentally, the quickest route around a track. But it just might be the most fun.

Therein lies the joy of track days. It's up to you really. There are those perfectionists who will want to hone their driving skills, talk oversteer and understeer all day, and finally be rewarded by shaving precious seconds off their track times. For those who normally purr about town in Porsches it's a chance to find out what a performance car is like before the safety standards people get their way with it. For the people-carrier drivers of the world it's a chance to let rip in something where nobody ever mentions the lack of legroom in the back. Most of all it's a chance to cut loose, throw the rules out of the window and give it some welly.

Which is why you don't have to be a petrolhead to enjoy it. There is a deeply satisfying sense of lawlessness that comes with being given someone else's car, on a road with no speed limits, extensive run offs, and big piles of tyres to remind you exactly where to crash.

Of course if you are a petrolhead then you will be in seventh heaven. You can pretend to be Clarkson pontificating at the wheel of a Ferrari (it takes all sorts) or experience the feel of a Lotus Elise seemingly gripping the road by a weird combination of ground effect and will power. You can even get in a single seat racer and have your life flash in front of your eyes while the track flashes by inches from your bum.

Go go-karting

Personally though, my favourite petrol fuelled experiences are a little slower, though no less exciting for that. The first is go-karting, which has come a long way since the pedal-powered contraption you piloted when in short trousers. Modern go-karts are torque monsters with all the poke you need to go flying round the bends. Best of all they come with something that most other track day experiences don't – opposition. Go-karting is one of the few motor events where you'll safely be allowed to race even if you've never even been behind the wheel before.

It doesn't matter where you choose to go go-karting – there is a certain ritual to be observed.

1. You will be expected to don flameproof suits and helmets
2. There will be an obligatory Ralf Schumacher joke
3. There will be straw bales
4. There will be lots of rules explained including those about cheating
5. You will pay about as much attention to these as you do the airplane safety instructions
6. You will wait at the start line up with a dinky little traffic light to set you off
7. Fleetwood Mac will be played (F1 fans will tell you why)
8. You will overshoot your first corner
9. The red mist will come down over your eyes
10. You will gently nudge your best friend's offside bumper, thus sending him pirouetting into those straw bales
11. Someone will wave a flag at you at this point
12. You will win, only to find that you were disqualified (it was in the rules but you were looking at your own reflection at the time)
13. You will have to be restrained from doing a James Hunt (no it's not rhyming slang)

Skid marks

Go-karting is a blast, and yet still only my second favourite car-related outing. The best for me is the skid pan. Everyone should have a go at the skid pan because it not only features fairground volume shrieking (or is that just me?), but it actually teaches you something.

Skid pans can be misnomers. Some do involve a skiddy surface for you to spin wildly across but the more sophisticated ones feature a frame around the car which looks oddly as if the car is wearing very large dental braces. The frame has its own set of wheels and can put pressure onto them. The idea is that is gives a precise way of taking a bit of grip off the real wheels so the instructor can decide just how much and what type of skid to give you. After that you learn the art of steering into a skid while the car seemingly takes a fancy to that brick wall over there. Brilliant.

Three Sisters Race Circuit

Three Sisters Race Circuit is the ideal venue to enter the exhilarating world of motor sport.

We have been teaching people to drive race cars since 1978 and are a founder member of The Association of Racing Drivers' Schools.

We provide motor sport experiences from £35 up to £1200, 70 mph pro karting to driving a real Formula One car.

Experiences:

Karting:
Three Sisters is the UK's longest and fastest kart circuit. Our pro karts are capable of up to 70 mph. Are you?

Racing Experience:
Experience the thrill, sensation and speed of driving a full-specification single-seat racing car by booking one of our Racing Experience trials. Full training will be given in a sports saloon car.

Super Car Experience:
If you have ever dreamed of driving the fabulous Ferrari 360 Modena or the superb Porsche 911 Turbo, then fulfil your dreams. The Ferrari is truly beautiful and with a whopping 400bhp, it can be a handful! The Porsche is very different – a fine demonstration of German excellence, it's the ultimate everyday supercar.

Formula One Experience:
This is simply the driving experience of a lifetime. Few people have been able to experience the raw power and ultimate driving experience of a Formula One car.

Our 600bhp F1 car was raced by the current Ferrari Formula One Test Driver Luca Badoer. This exclusive driving experience is very intimate and includes a great deal of tuition to prepare you for a life-changing day!

Activity Location:
North West

Contact Details:
Three Sisters Race Circuit
T: 01942 270230
E: info@racing-school.co.uk
W: www.racing-school.co.uk

Vouchers:
All our driving activities are available as an open-dated gift voucher. Please contact us for further details

Corporate Events:
Exclusive corporate events are available incorporating all our activities and a full catering package

Practical:
Age, height and weight restrictions do apply, please contact us for details on each particular experience
Three Sisters Race Circuit is approved by the Motor Sports Association (MSA), the governing body of motor sport in Great Britain

Special Offer/Incentive
A 10% discount is available for readers of *Ultimate Gift Experiences*. Cannot be combined with any other discount or promotional offer.

★ **10% DISCOUNT** Please mention *Ultimate Gift Experiences* when booking

Buckmore Park Karting Limited

To experience the thrill of real outdoor karting, why not head for Chatham's 1200 metre Buckmore Park Kart Circuit in Kent. This beautifully situated floodlit venue is Europe's market leader in competition, corporate and youngsters karting. A session at Buckmore will be a day to remember. Over 150 karts for hire.

Activity Location:
South East

Contact Details:
Buckmore Park Karting Ltd
T: 01634 201562
E: sales@buckmore.co.uk
W: www.buckmore.co.uk

Practical Information:
Ages 5–80! Height restriction, children min. 4ft 2in, adults 5ft

Equipment:
Over 150 vehicles for hire – group off-road and karts

Availability:
Open 7 days a week, 8am to 10pm, all year round

Gift Vouchers:
Gift vouchers available in £5 and £20 denominations

Corporate:
For exclusive corporate group enquiries contact sales on 01634 661600

Special Offer/Incentive
£5 off entry into a specified Buckmore 600 event. Valid for one person for one transaction only. Please quote DE600 when booking.

★ **£5 DISCOUNT** (see above)
When you quote REF. DE600

Experiences:

- *30-Minute Hire Practice Session.* The ideal introduction to karting. 30-minute practice sessions. Choice of either 70 mph or 80 mph karts
- *Buckmore 600 Grand Prix.* Monthly event on 600 metre South Circuit. Practice, three heats and final per driver
- *Buckmore 1200 Grand Prix.* Monthly event on 1200 metre International Circuit. Practice, three heats and A&B finals
- *Iron Man/Man of Steel 1 Hr Individual Enduro.* Monthly event on 1200 metre International Circuit. 70 mph or 80 mph Karts. Timed qualifying and one hour individual enduro
- *2 Hr/3 Hr/6 Hr Team Enduro.* Monthly team events. Choice of 70 mph or 80 mph Karts. Timed qualifying and continuous enduro race
- *Exclusive Group Grand Prix.* Minimum group size 12. Maximum group size 48. Practice, heats and final
- *Exclusive Group Multi Activity Day.* Minimum group size 12. Maximum group size 48. Off-road activities (quads, powerturns, argocats) plus Karting Grand Prix. All day event
- *Youngsters Arrive 'n' Drive/Birthday Parties/Kart School and Junior Club.* Arrive 'n' drive karting for youngsters aged 8+. Exclusive birthday parties, Kart Racing School and Junior Club. Passenger rides for children aged 5+ in our twin-seat kart

Castle Combe Racing School Ltd

Castle Combe Circuit is situated in the heart of Wiltshire, just five miles west of Chippenham, and is one of the longest established circuits in the UK. A wide range of activities are available at the circuit throughout the year; these include car and motorcycle racing, driving experiences, rally driving, track days, action days and corporate days including circuit hire.

Experiences:

- *Super Saloon Driving Experience.* A fantastic taster course where you drive a saloon car followed by a white-knuckle ride in the Subaru Impreza WRX
- *Single Seater Driving Experience.* Experience the thrill of driving the Formula Ford racing car with our Single Seater Driving Experience
- *Single Seater Advanced Driving Experience.* All the excitement of the Single Seater Driving Experience but with lots more driving!
- *Sports Saloon Driving Experience.* Time to get sporty by driving the Subaru Impreza WRX and Lotus Elise
- *Sports Saloon Advanced Driving Experience.* All of the above course with further tuition in both the Subaru Impreza WRX and Lotus Elise
- *Lotus Elise Sports and Racing Driving Experience.* Time to do it all! Drive the saloon car, the Formula Ford racing car, the Subaru Impreza and the Lotus Elise - awesome
- *Rally Drive.* Experience the excitement of rallying on the special gravel rally stage
- *Choice of White Knuckle Rides.* Experience the thrill of your life with a high-speed passenger ride. Choose from the Ferrari Modena 360, Lotus Elise or Subaru Impreza WRX

Activity Location:
South West

Contact Details:
Castle Combe Racing School Ltd
T: 01249 782417
E: sales@castlecombecircuit.co.uk
W: www.castlecombecircuit.co.uk

Gift Vouchers:
Gift vouchers are available, all open-dated vouchers valid for 12 months

Groups:
Group bookings welcome, contact the office to check availability

Special Offer:
Single Seater Driving Experience
Castle Combe Circuit would like to offer *Ultimate Gift Experience* readers a special offer of £30 off the Single Seater Driving Experience. Please quote the following reference UGESS125 when booking.

★ **£30 DISCOUNT** (see above)
When you quote REF: UGESS125

Daytona

Daytona have been setting the standards of kart racing in the UK for 15 years and are proud to have three prestigious venues across the UK. The Daytona Milton Keynes International Circuit is recognised as one of the longest and most demanding kart circuits in the UK, while the smaller, tight and twisty North Circuit is well suited for small groups as well as an excellent junior training facility. Within the M25, Daytona Sandown Park is both a fast and challenging circuit, based in the centre of the beautifully landscaped horse race course. Both of these circuits are outdoors while Daytona Manchester is recognised as *the* indoor circuit in the UK offering unparalleled facilities.

Activity Location:
Surrey, Milton Keynes, Manchester

Contact Details:
Daytona
T: 0845 6445501
E: sales@daytona.co.uk
W: www.daytona.co.uk

Practical Information:
We recommend you wear comfortable clothing with flat, soft-soled shoes, ideally trainers. You can drive at Daytona from 8 to 80 years of age.

Equipment:
All safety equipment will be provided, including racing suits, helmets and gloves

Availability:
Throughout the year – however, we do recommend booking in advance

Vouchers:
Prices start at £20 and are valid for one year from the date of purchase

Corporate events:
We operate bespoke corporate packages; please get in touch to discuss requirements

Special Offer
A 10% discount on all non-exclusive events when you quote Ref. DEYB. Cannot be combined with any other discounts or promotional offers

★ 10% DISCOUNT
When you quote REF: DEYB

Experiences:

All of the following are available at all Daytona Circuits

- *Arrive and Drive.* Just phone and pre-book your 30 minute arrive and drive sessions
- *Corporate Events.* Daytona is recognised as market leader in running high quality corporate kart racing events. We will work with you in hosting and entertaining your guests to the highest standards, with in-house catering to meet all of your requirements
- *Open Races.* Join in open races, individually or as part of a group and take on the challenge of a heat plus final race competition
- *Endurance Races.* Can you take on the challenge, do you have the stamina for an endurance race? We have a selection of endurance races lasting from 30 minutes to 24 hours
- *Championship Races.* So you want to be a champion? Join in our monthly In Kart Championship and prove you really are the best
- *Junior Parties.* Hold a fabulous birthday party for children as young as 8 yrs old, full tuition given on the day in a fun and safe environment
- *Junior Race School.* So you have a budding Button! We hold race schools for juniors on a regular basis, providing young wannabe racing drivers the opportunity to learn their craft from the very basics to winning races

Croft Circuit

Croft Circuit offers the best driving experiences in the North of England. Offering the chance to drive Porsches, Ferraris, Caterhams and Minis, for all abilities. Whether you want to indulge yourself, buy a gift for someone else, hold a corporate day, team-building day or product launch, Croft can cater for individuals or groups of between 16 and 50 people.

Experiences:

New Starter Experience/Duration 2 hrs and 30 mins:
If you do not hold a driving licence, but want to experience the controls of a car in a safe environment, this is the ideal course. The experience starts with a briefing in vehicle controls and road safety. You then take the wheel with an Approved Driving Standards Instructor and master basic skills. The course ends by driving on the 2.12 mile international circuit.

Caterham 7 Experience/Duration 2 hrs and 15 mins:
Safety briefing and circuit familiarisation. The instructor drives the Caterham for two familiarisation laps, guest drives for five laps x 2 sessions, followed by a high-speed passenger ride of one lap by the instructor.

Porsche 911 & Ginetta G20 Experience/Duration 2 hrs and 15 mins:
A safety briefing and circuit familiarisation. Familiarisation laps by the instructor in the Ginetta G20. Guest drives Ginetta G20 six laps, Porsche 911 six laps, followed by a high-speed passenger drive of one lap by the instructor.

Ferrari Super 4 Experience/Duration 3 hrs:
Safety briefing and circuit familiarisation in Mini Cooper S, instructor drives. Guest drives Ginetta G20 four laps, Mini Cooper S four laps, Porsche 911 three laps, Ferrari 328 GTB three laps, followed by a high-speed performance ride of one lap by the instructor

Minimum age 21 yrs.

Activity Location:
North East

Contact details:
Croft Circuit
T: 01325 721815
E: enquiries@croftcircuit.co.uk
W: www.croftcircuit.co.uk

Gift Vouchers:
Gift Vouchers are available for all experiences; individual vouchers carry an expiry date

Practical Information:
New Starter Experience is for participants of 13 yrs +, maximum height 6ft 4in, maximum weight restrictions 16 stone
All other experiences participants must be 18 yrs + and carry a full driving licence. (Except Ferrari experience – 21yrs +)
Minimum height 5ft 2in, maximum height 6ft 4in
Maximum weight 18 stone

Drive Tech Limited

Drive Tech Limited operates within the grounds of the Castle Combe Race Circuit, Chippenham, Wiltshire. We have been providing driving activities for over 18 years and specialise in skid control, 4×4 off-road driving and 200cc outdoor karting. We can accommodate individuals, small or large groups, birthday parties, stag and hen parties and corporate team building/staff incentives.

Activity Location:
South West

Contact Details:
Drive Tech Ltd
T: 01249 783010
E: info@combe-events.co.uk
W: www.combe-events.co.uk

Corporate:
Tailored to individual requirements and budget. Please contact us for further information

Special Offer/Incentive:
10% discount off our 4×4 off-road driving course and/or 10% off when purchasing 2 adult kart gift vouchers
Vouchers valid for 18 months from date of purchase
Quote reference DE/DTECH06 when booking

Experiences:

Skid Control Training:
Defensive Driver Training course aiming to teach full licence holders how to control a vehicle in icy or slippery road conditions. Our ADI instructors (or equivalent) teach a three hour course in our vehicles (front and rear wheel drive) all the disciplines required in a group learning environment. The course is both informative and excellent fun.

4×4 Off-Road Driving:
Learn the skill of off-road driving in our Land Rover Discoveries with our BORDA (British Off-Road Driving Association) accredited instructors. Tough, but user-friendly course aiming to teach all the techniques used in 4×4 driving. Full driving licence required.

200cc Outdoor Karting:
Exhilarating fun in 200cc Honda karts on a 350m outdoor track, with 'grippy' SMA tarmac surface giving you both speed and control. Grand Prix formats for individuals and groups on our public kart Grand Prix, which run most Saturday afternoons. Private events available for exclusive use groups in either Endurance or GP formats.

Also Junior Kart Racing School on 1st and 3rd Sunday mornings for 10–15 year olds (min. height 4ft 8in).

★ **10% DISCOUNT** (see above)
When you quote REF: DE/DTECH06

Incarace Ltd

Incarace is the largest stock car racing promoter in the UK, with three of the main tracks in the country.

Stock car experience racedays take place at Northampton International Raceway, off junction 15 M1, an hour from London and Birmingham.

Activity Location:
Midlands

Contact Details:
Incarace Ltd
T: 01650 511977
E: markbond@incarace.co.uk
W: www.incarace.co.uk

Availability:
Please call 01650 511977 for availability and booking

Special Offer/Incentive:
A 10% discount if you quote the booking code MB06. Cannot be combined with any other discounts or promotional offers.

Experiences:

Stock Car Multi Activity Race Day:
Real motor racing in *real* racing cars on a *real* racing track!

This full-day event is fantastic value and offers individuals and groups the chance to race in real stock cars, with all of the pizzazz of a real stock car event! A must for all budding racers. You will also experience the awesome Professionals Big Blast, the fantastic Del Boy Challenge and the hysterical Nag Drag!

- Real motor racing, the next step from karting
- A full-day event, fantastic value
- Practice sessions, heat sessions, feature finals
- At least three other great events including the Del Boy Challenge, the Nag Drag and the Professionals Challenge – awesome!
- Enthusiastic instructors, excitable commentators, trophies, colour race programme, lunch included. A wonderful day out for all the family

★ **10% DISCOUNT**
When you quote REF: MB06

Knockhill Racing Circuit

Fans of two and four wheel motorsport already know that Knockhill Racing Circuit in Fife is Scotland's National Motorsport Centre and leading venue at some of Britain's best racing championships. This popular venue boasts a myriad of driving thrills, from Single Seater Race cars to a 'dream come true' Ferrari course at the wheel of a stunning flame-red 175-mph Italian supercar.

Activity Location:
Scotland

Contact details:
Knockhill Racing
T: 01383 720044
E: enquiries@knockhill.com
W: www.knockhill.com

Practical Information:
Drivers must hold full UK licence, karting from 8yrs+, Passenger Thrill Rides from 10yrs+

Availability:
Open 7 days. Booking is essential

Gift Vouchers:
Gift vouchers available from £99

Corporates:
Call 01383 720044 to discuss your individual requirements

Special Offers:
A 10% discount is available for readers of *Ultimate Gift Experiences*. Cannot be combined with any other discount or promotional offer.

★ **10% DISCOUNT** Please mention *Ultimate Gift Experiences* when booking

Experiences:

- *Skid Control.* A real driver survival course
- *4×4 Off-Road Course.* Drive yourself wild in a 'top of the range' John R. Weir Jeep Cherokee
- *SEAT & Single Seater Experiences.* For high-speed adrenaline and a true Formula One style experience. Drive solo in one of our brand new Honda Blackbird motorcycle-engined Single Seaters for an awesome driving experience
- *Rally Experience.* It's a sideways world. Well, it is on our purpose-built rally stage (as driven by Colin McRae). Our fully qualified instructors will encourage you to drive in a way you never dreamt possible. Pure adrenaline
- *Ultimate Passenger Thrill Rides.* Book your seat in 'first class' for the *ultimate* passenger thrill ride. Combine the best of race and rally cars in our stunning Ferrari 355, unique F1 racing car and our fantastic Ford Focus rally car
- *Ferrari 355 Experience.* Your chance to live the dream. Hold your breath as you hear the unmistakable roar of the 380bhp, 40-valve V8 engine. It's your chance to drive the fabulous Ferrari 355. Guaranteed to be an unforgettable experience
- *Ultimate Drivers Experience.* The perfect blend SEAT and Single Seater Experience skid challenge. Relax in our restaurant with a two-course lunch and shake it up on our rally experience. We recommend that everyone should experience the *ultimate* day out
- Plus many more!

Steve Robertson Training Services - Lorry Driver Training

We specialise in training drivers for:

- Large goods vehicles
- Passenger carrying vehicles
- Fork lift truck operators (counterbalance and reach)
- Lorry-mounted crane operators (HIAB)
- Rough-terrain telescopic handler
- LGV theory training in our well-equipped classroom

Activity Location:
South West

Contact Details:
Steve Robertson
E: lorrydrivertraining@tiscali.co.uk
W: www.lorrydrivertraining.co.uk

Practical Information:
Because the driving is off-road there is no need to hold a provisional LGV licence – a normal car licence is OK
A certificate of achievement will be issued at the end of the session

Availability:
For more information or to book please email lorrydrivertraining@tiscali.co.uk

Corporate:
Daily rates for corporate entertainment available on request.

Experiences:

Established in Devon since 1990, we have always specialised solely in training LGV and PCV drivers.

Always wanted to drive an artic?

We can arrange an off-road session driving a 38 ton artic for a special treat or surprise present. The training vehicle is a realistic-sized lorry, 16.5 metres long, 360 HP with 16 gears, complete with a 45ft 3-axle trailer.

Many people have said they have 'always fancied a go at driving a large articulated lorry'. Well, we can arrange this for you at Westpoint in Exeter. Westpoint is a realistic road layout (covering approx. 20 acres) complete with traffic lights, road junctions, pedestrian crossings, etc.

We offer a 2-hour Articulated Vehicle Driving Experience. The package includes a 30-minute commentary drive by an LGV driving instructor, followed by a hands-on driving session at Westpoint for approximately one hour. The instructor will then drive the lorry back to the yard.

Manby Motorplex

Manby Motorplex, established in the 1980s, is a driving experience and training centre as well as a popular motor sport venue. See www.manbymotorplex.com to fully appreciate the facilities at this former RAF airfield. The instructors are professional and safe but, as importantly, enthusiastic, friendly and helpful.

Activity Location:
Lincolnshire

Contact Details:
Manby Motorplex
T: 01472 816595
E: sales@manbymotorplex.com
W: www.manbymotorplex.com

Gift Vouchers:
Available to buy as a specific experience or as a sum towards a course of the recipient's own choosing

Corporate/Groups:
Excellent bespoke packages available – see www.manbymotorplex.com for full details

Discounts:
Check www.manbymotorplex.com for last-minute bargains, information on student discounts and to take advantage of the permanent online booking discount

Special Offer/Incentive:
Quote promotional code UGE07 to receive a 20% discount when booking online at www.manbymotorplex.com. Valid until December 2007. Not valid for use for taster courses, special offers or last-minute deals.

★ **20% DISCOUNT** (see above)
When you quote REF: UGE07

Experiences:

- *Rallying.* Using real competition 205GTi rally cars we give participants the opportunity to learn and practice rallying techniques. Courses are available to suit your ambition and pocket
- *Skid.* We pride ourselves on providing invaluable tuition in a professional but fun way. ROSPA approved
- *4×4 Off-Road.* An area of 100 acres gives plenty to get to grips with for both more experienced and novice 4×4 drivers alike. Experiences include one to one instruction and half and full day adventures
- *Big Toys.* Fulfil a lifelong dream to drive an HGV/artic lorry, a double-decker bus, MJ Bedford army truck or even a fire engine!
- *Junior Driving.* Keen to start before they are 17? We have courses giving good initial tuition from a top-rated ADI instructor. Alternatively, your youngster may enjoy trying the junior rally or 4×4 experiences
- *Multi-Activity.* Can't settle on just one experience? Opt for a multi-activity experience, making the most of your Manby visit

See www.manbymotorplex.com for details.

Mithril Racing at Goodwood Motor Circuit

For over 20 years Mithril has been providing driving thrills in a range of classic, racing and super cars at Britain's most historic and picturesque circuit – Goodwood, home of the famous Revival Meeting. We also have a Tiger Moth biplane for 'hands on' flights.

Experiences:

- *Ferrari Drive.* Three laps around Goodwood behind the wheel of a scintillating Ferrari
- *Lamborghini!* Drive Goodwood's sweeping high-speed corners in a hugely powerful Lamborghini
- *Single Seater.* Scorch around Goodwood's 2½-mile track in a proper racing car ... after demonstration laps and practice laps in an Alfa Romeo sports saloon
- *Classic Cars.* Get behind the wheel of three of the following: a lithe Porsche 911 RS rep, a cool Aston Martin DB4, a svelte Jaguar E-type or a thunderous Cobra
- *Super Cars – Lamborghini Diablo, Ferrari 355, Porsche 911.* These three ultimate supercars are yours for three laps each around the historic Goodwood Circuit
- *Slicks and Spokes.* A driver's dream. First instruction in Alfa Romeo sports saloon and then practice laps. Then drive a single-seater racing car, with slicks and wings. Then drive *two* of the following ... E-type Jaguar, Cobra V- 8, Aston Martin DB4, Chevrolet Corvette or Porsche 911
- *Tiger Moth Biplane.* Take to the skies at the wartime airfield of Goodwood in the plane that trained many of the 'few' ... the Tiger Moth
- *Vette and Viper.* Three laps in a monstrously powerful Dodge Viper and then three in a storming Chevrolet Corvette

Activity Location:
South East

Contact Details:
Mithril Racing at Goodwood Motor Circuit
T: 01243 528815
E: chris@mithril.co.uk
W: www.mithril.co.uk

Corporate:
Please call 01243 528815 or visit www.mithril.co.uk

Special Offer/Incentive:
A 10% discount is available when you quote DE06 during booking. Cannot be combined with any other offers or promotional discounts.

★ 10% DISCOUNT
When you quote REF: DE06

Rockingham Motor Speedway

In just five years Rockingham has become more than just a motor sport facility. It has become one of the top entertainment venues in the Midlands and the UK.

Rockingham is a multi faceted business with a wealth of experience and expertise in every sector including corporate driving days, manufacturer track and venue hire, driver training, conference and banqueting for up to 500 delegates, meeting room and suite hire, motor racing and of course, individual driving experiences.

Activity Location:
Midlands

Contact Details:
The Race School Rockingham
T: 01536 271272
E: experiences@rockingham.co.uk
W: www.rockingham.co.uk

Practical Information:
Crash helmets will be provided

Availability:
Operational from February to November, 1-2 days per month, normally on a Saturday

Gift Vouchers:
Gift Vouchers can be purchased for an experience, which are valid for 12 months

Experiences:

- *High Speed Passenger Ride*. This isn't about driving, it's about screaming with excitement as the professional driver takes to the track at breakneck speed and scares you witless!
- *Mini Cooper S Experience*. A supercharged MINI adventure around Rockingham's challenging infield circuit is so much fun
- *Skid Car Experience*. Using techniques that simulate loss of car control you'll learn the skills (and thrills) of driving on ice, aquaplaning and skid avoidance exercises
- *4x4 Off-Road Experience*. Learn how to handle the wildest off-road situations on this fantastic man-made course
- *Ferrari 360 Experience*. As you settle into the driver's seat of the Ferrari you know you are experiencing something very special
- *Porsche 911 Turbo Experience*. The eternal supercar – nothing looks or drives like it! The wailing, rear-mounted flat-six engine delivers awesome power in a truly unique manner
- *Formula Rockingham Circuit Experience*. A chance to drive a Grand Prix-style single seater round the challenging high-speed and technical low-geared corners of the Rockingham Circuit
- *Ultimate Supercar Experience*. We've combined four of the world's top supercars to create the ultimate experience. The Ferrari 360, Porsche 911 Turbo, Porsche Boxster S and the Lotus Elise

Staffs Rider Training

Whether you're a novice rider or returning to biking after a break we have the knowledge to help you improve your skills and enjoy riding safely. We take training seriously. We know you want the best instruction and know you will find your course informative and enjoyable. All our instructors are trained to the highest standards so you are in very safe hands with our professional team.

Activity Location:
Midlands

Contact Details:
Staffs Rider Training
T: 01827 286660
E: das@staffsridertraining.com
W: www.staffsridertraining.com

Practical Information:
Min. age 16 yrs

Equipment:
All equipment is provided

Availability:
Open 7 days per week all year round

Corporates/Groups:
Please call our office

Special Offer/Incentive:
A 10% discount is available when you quote UGI2006.

Experiences:

Compulsory basic training (CBT):
This is a 6-8 hour course covering motorcycle safety, clothing and basic maintenance checks. Training begins in the safety of our off-road training area, then you progress to a 2 hour, radio linked, supervised road training and evaluation ride. The CBT certificate allows you to ride legally on the road according to your age and licence restrictions.

Direct Access Courses (DAC):
Depending upon the ability of the rider we offer courses of between two and five days of intensive training. This course is one instructor to two students and is only conducted by DAS-approved instructors. The test is taken on a motorcycle exceeding 47bhp and will give the rider an unrestricted licence.

Back to Biking:
Ideal for both motorcyclists who have passed the DSA test and who want to progress to a larger machine, and those who already have a full licence and wish to return to motorcycling.

★ 10% DISCOUNT
When you quote REF: UGI2006

Thruxton Motorsport Centre

Welcome to the fastest racetrack in the UK, and one of the longest at 2.4 miles. Combined with a jaw-dropping fleet of supercars including Ferrari, Porsche and Lamborghini plus racing cars, karting, flying, 4×4 driving and over 25 years of experience, Thruxton Motorsport Centre is the premier choice for driving experiences in the UK. In addition we also have an exhilarating outdoor kart centre.

Activity Location:
South West

Contact Details:
Thruxton Motorsport Centre
T: 01264 882222
E: info@thruxtonracing.co.uk
W: www.thruxtonracing.co.uk

Practical Information:
We have no age restrictions; drivers need to hold a full and current driving licence

Equipment:
All safety equipment will be provided, including helmets, gloves and racing boots

Availability:
Experiences are available on selected weekdays and weekends throughout the year

Gift packs and vouchers:
Prices start at £80 and are valid for 1 year from the date of purchase

Corporate events:
We operate bespoke corporate packages; please get in touch to discuss requirements

Our policy:
We promise to always have the latest supercars from Ferrari, Porsche, Lamborghini and Aston Martin

Special Offer
A 10% discount is available on all driving experiences when you quote Ref. TXNDX. Cannot be combined with any other discounts or promotional offers.

★ 10% DISCOUNT
When you quote REF: TXNDX

Experiences:

- *Racing Car.* Slicks and wings racing cars – feel like an F1 driver in these sophisticated single seaters
- *Ferrari Experiences.* Everyone should drive a Ferrari at least once. Enjoy the iconic Ferrari 355 and the latest model, the F430
- *Porsche 911 Turbo.* The everyday supercar. It doesn't matter how many you see on the road, the power of this car will amaze you
- *Lamborghini.* Huge engine, scissor doors and out of this world styling, everything you'd expect from Lamborghini
- *Italian and Ultimate Supercar Experiences.* Finally the age-old question of which is better - Lamborghini or Ferrari - can be answered
- *One-To-One.* Lots of track time in our track-focused cars, Lotus Exige, racing saloons and two-seat sports cars
- *Young MINI Experiences.* The MINI is back and better than ever. Learn to drive before you have a licence. Gain the essential car control skills needed to pass the driving test
- *4×4 Off-Road Driving.* Take a lot of water, mud, steep hills and the latest off-road vehicle and experience the challenge and fun of driving off-road

Vision Motorsport Ltd

We are a company specialising in motor sport driving events designed to thrill! We operate from a very authentic off-road venue, which has a fantastic loose surface rally stage and a challenging 4×4 course. We also operate at venues in the north and south for our Performance Car programs. Great value for money experiences.

Experiences:

- *Rally Driving – 2 Wheel Drive.* A half or full day of fun in our front-wheel-drive rally cars which will really test your skills. Are you up to the challenge?
- *Rally Driving – 4 Wheel Drive.* A half or full day programme in the powerful Subaru Impreza WRX
- *Junior Rally Driving.* A half day course. Start them young and let them go rallying for real! (Age 11–17, min. height 4'6")
- *4×4 Off-Road Driving.* A half or full day course. Our off-road driving adventures will test your driving skills to the limit
- *Performance Cars.* A half day program. Drive five of the world's fastest production sports cars. Typically the Ferrari 360, Porsche 996, Audi RS4, Subaru Impreza WRX and Lotus Elise
- *1000HP+.* A two hour program. WOW! Your opportunity to drive some of the world's fastest and most awesome sports cars. Typically the Ferrari 360, Porsche 996, Subaru Impreza WRX and Lotus Elise
- *Ride & Drive.* A one hour program. Drive and be driven in two high-performance sports cars – strap in tight!

Activity Location:
North East (tarmac events only) and South Central (rally, 4×4 and tarmac events)

Contact Details:
Vision Motorsport
T: 0870 750 4100
E: sales@visionmotorsport.co.uk
W: www.visionmotorsport.co.uk

Practical Information:
Age/height/weight restrictions apply to most activities, please visit our website or contact us for further details

Equipment:
All safety equipment required will be provided

Availability:
Our office is open 9am–5pm Monday to Saturday
Rally and 4×4 events operate all year round
Tarmac events operate March to December

Gift voucher information:
All gift vouchers are valid for 12 months

Corporate:
Corporate events are available for groups of 8+, please contact us for a quotation based on your requirements

Special Offer/Incentive:
Ultimate Gift Experience customers receive a 10% discount on all of our activities when booked on line at www.visionmotorsport.co.uk quoting Promotion Code: UGE06.

★ **10% DISCOUNT** (see above)
When you quote REF: UGE06

Everyman Motor Racing Activities

The world of high-performance cars never stands still. At Everyman Motor Racing we pride ourselves on always being on pole position. We were the first to introduce Formula One Driving Experiences, Ferrari and Supercar Challenges, entry-level Mini Cooper courses and much more.

We look forward to welcoming you and your friends on a day they will never forget.

Activity Location:
Midlands

Contact Details:
Everyman Motor Racing Activities
T: 01455 841670
E: info@everymanracing.co.uk
W: www.ferraridriving.com

Practical information:
All drivers must hold a valid UK or International driving licence
Height and weight restrictions apply

Availability:
Selected weekdays and weekends throughout the year

Gift Vouchers:
Available for all occasions

Corporate and Group bookings:
Available upon request

Special Offer/Incentive:
A 10% discount is available – please quote DE06 when booking. Cannot be combined with any other discounts or promotional offers.

★ 10% DISCOUNT
When you quote REF: DE06

Experiences:

- *Ferrari, Aston Martin, Porsche and Lamborghini Driving.* You can drive any or all of these supercars on one of our superb track driving experiences. Some of the most evocative names in motor racing all under one roof
- *Le Mans Classic Cars.* The golden age of motoring is back with an unforgettable day behind the wheel. Drivers experience cars that don't just turn heads but stir the soul
- *Mini Mayhem.* Today's new Minis are more agile and fun than ever. Let us put you behind the wheel of one of our most popular courses, inspired by the classic 60s film *The Italian Job*
- *Rally Courses.* There really is no greater test of a driver's skills or for that matter, their nerve!
- *Off-Road Events.* Set in the grounds of beautiful Belvoir Castle you can experience everything from hovercraft driving, tanks, helicopter rides and stroll around the castle – a real family day out
- *Formula One Driving.* F1 is the ultimate driving experience and a rare opportunity to experience what only Schumacher, Button, Senna and an exclusive few have. A two-day event for that very special occasion

Circuit Based Training Ltd

Pass your motorbike test with confidence at the UK's only track-based, DSA-approved training school. Established in 1997 at Donnington Park, we have now moved to Mallory Park and Prestwold Hall. Our highly acclaimed courses have been reviewed by *Bike Magazine* (5 stars) and *MCN*.

Activity Location:
East Midlands

Contact Details:
Circuit Based Training Ltd
T: 01455 840645
W: www.circuitbasedtraining.co.uk

Practical Information:
Full motorcycle clothing must be worn (knee sliders are optional)
Clients' bikes must be safe and roadworthy

Availability:
Please contact Circuit Based Training on 01455 840645 to book

Special Offer/Incentive:
A 10% discount is available for readers of *Ultimate Gift Experiences*. Cannot be combined with any other discount or promotional offer.

Experiences:

- *CBT Courses*. This is your first objective. No one can progress onto the motorcycle test without first earning a CBT certificate. Includes familiarisation with the controls of the bike, starting, stopping, slow riding, manoeuvring around cones, emergency stops, cornering techniques, counter steering, pivot steering, ideal reference points, suspension set up and emergency braking in the bends. The course is completed with a two hour assessment on public roads
- *DAS Courses*. We specialise in Direct Access training, gaining a full, unrestricted motorcycle licence for clients over 21 years. We will ensure you become a safe, confident and competent rider while providing an environment where you can learn at your own pace and pass your test, knowing you can handle any bike in the showroom. Your full test will take place on the final day
- *Refresher Courses*. Designed for those with a full licence who have not ridden for some time or as a confidence booster
- *Advanced Cornering Course*. The course concentrates on the finer aspects of cornering, to enable each rider to become more consistent in their assessment and execution of cornering at speed
- *Advanced Road Course*. For new or experienced riders who want to improve their overall road riding. This course concentrates on cornering, overtaking and making safe progress on public roads

★ **10% DISCOUNT** Please mention *Ultimate Gift Experiences* when booking

Flying

'Nobody can be uncheered with a balloon.'

WINNIE THE POOH, COURTESY OF A.A. MILNE

Reach for the skies

Aerobatics, helicopters, ballooning, gliders, microlights, Tiger Moth, flying lessons.

They call it the microlight grin. The corners of your mouth hurt, you have squashed flies on your teeth and you'll be talking about it all day, just as soon as you get your breath back and your heart rate looks more like a score from basketball than from cricket.

Man has always wanted to fly. It is literally one of our commonest dreams and has been from the day the first caveman looked up. These days there have never been more ways of getting airborne, or more varieties of experience from the full-on Biggles to the more soul-satisfying silences of gliding and ballooning.

Powered flight

When I was a kid I made an Airfix model of a de Havilland Tiger Moth. Of course it was held together with stringy glue and looked like the wings would drop off at any moment. Which is astonishingly lifelike as it happens. The real Tiger Moth took to the air at the very beginning of the 1930s and, due to the shortages of the depression era, it was made entirely from recycled kiss-me-quick hats and the string taken from the binding of the *Boy's Own Annual*. The result is brilliant and the story goes that many dedicated Moth pilots are commercial airline pilots taking a break from the computerised, sanitised world of modern flight. Certainly there's nothing sanitised about being in a biplane, whether it's a Moth or one of the many acrobatic biplanes on the fun-flying circuit. Not only do you get to wear goggles and shout 'contact' but you can also go 'dacka-dacka-dacka' as you dive and quite possibly bomb the lush countryside below with what was once your lunch.

If you thought the Moth was a blast, and the most unlikely way of taking to the air then your next step is to go for a trial ride in a microlight. Microlights make Moths look like something Ferdinand Porsche might have come up with if he worked for NASA. If it looks like a hang-glider with an engine bolted on the back that's because it is.

At least in the Moth you are sitting *in* something. As you are asked to strap into a microlight behind the pilot you realise that all that's keeping you attached to the airframe is a seat and a seat-belt. If you really want to scare yourself you'll check out the chewing gum and rubber bands that hold the seat to the rest of the plane. It's like taking to the air on a piece of scaffolding kept in the sky entirely by an oversized handkerchief. Take off is the moment of true intestinal clench as your pilot guns the mighty engine (think pizza delivery special with no silencer) and the grass flashes by beneath you. Then suddenly you're up and climbing at a rate more normally associated with high-speed lifts. And it's all surprisingly calm and stable. So stable in fact that your pilot is contractually bound to demonstrate that he/she can take their hands off the control bar altogether and the craft will still maintain a true course. You will hear a faint buzzing in the headphones at this point. That's the pilot pointing out that your fingernails are embedded in their shoulders and can they have their arms back please.

Silent splendours

Ballooning, on the other hand, is more like a state of mind than a means of getting airborne. While other forms of flight involve constant adjustment of controls, balloonists simply soar aloft and drift silently to whatever destination nature chooses for them.

You don't steer a balloon. That doesn't mean you have no control over where you're going – advanced knowledge of the likely winds and the ability to read air patterns means a balloon pilot can place their craft pretty accurately in the path of winds going the way they want. Other than rising or falling, however, that's the limit of the control. For some that sounds like a limitation. For others it is the ultimate liberation and the reason why ballooning makes more sense now than at any time in its long history.

Apart from the occasional whooshing noise of the propane burners when the pilot wants to rise higher, the beauty of ballooning is that you ride in spectacular silence. If you look below you there will be a chase car somewhere on the ground which is following you. When the balloon lands after a hard morning bobbing around it will be packed back into the car, which also provides transport back to where you started. Alternatively it may contain lunch and this is another beauty of ballooning. As a sport it is done in the morning before the sun heats the ground and sets off the thermals. This means that it dovetails beautifully with the art of gorging yourself in the countryside, without the risk that you're only going to lose your lunch on the return.

As the sun gets higher its effects are stronger and that means it heats up areas of the ground more. Hot patches of ground heat the air above them, which becomes less dense and rises causing cold air to rush in to fill the gap; there you get breezes and winds. Bad news for balloonists but excellent tidings for gliding.

Gliding is the most graceful, the most elegant and probably the slowest way of falling out of the sky we have yet invented. It's also fiendishly complicated and involves an elaborate game of three-dimensional chess played against invisible air currents. Unless you're just there for the ride of course, in which case you will probably never again feel so relaxed about being in a plane with no engine.

The Microlight Aviation Club

Since 1980 we've been running a very friendly microlight flying club and school at Popham Airfield in Hampshire.

Experiences:

Trial Flights and Flying Lessons:

- *Operation SKYLARK* (20 minutes). This twenty minute flight is designed to give you a brief introduction to the world of those who love and live to fly. During the flight, with your instructor's help, you'll be able to take the controls and fly the aeroplane yourself. This is the ideal way to see if microlight flying is for you
- *Operation KINGFISHER* (40 minutes). A forty minute version of the above for those who would like a bit more time in the air. On all these flights, if the conditions are suitable and you so wish, you'll be able to participate in both the takeoff and the landing phases as well as controlling the aeroplane during the rest of the flight
- *Operation PHOENIX* (60 minutes). A sixty minute flight where you'll be shown some of the more advanced techniques of flying the aeroplane – in fact you'll be flying the aeroplane yourself most of the time if that's what you want and this flight is long enough for us to sometimes land out at another site if conditions are suitable

Activity Location:
South Central

Contact Details:
The Microlight Aviation Club
T: 0845 130 9676
W: www.microlightflyingschool.co.uk

Practical Information:
All flying is subject to satisfactory weather conditions
Please wear sensible outdoor clothing. We provide thermal oversuits for cold weather, although most of the aircraft are heated. Flat shoes please
Max weight limit 16 st/102 kg
Please note, all our aircraft have enclosed cockpits and fixed, rigid wings, similar to a conventional light aircraft. We do not fly flex-wing microlights (hang-gliders with engines)

Availability:
Booking is essential. Please phone 0845 130 9676 during office hours.

Almat Flying Club

Feel the need to fly?

Why not come and join us. Experience the freedom and excitement of flying a light aircraft.

Activity Location:
Midlands

Contact Details:
Almat Flying Club
T: 02476 305519
E: info@almat.co.uk
W: www.almat.co.uk

Availability:
Booking is essential. Please contact us for more information

Practical Information:
Min. age 12 years
Flights are subject to weather conditions. We adhere to the standards, rules and regulations as laid down by The Civil Aviation Authority to ensure that you have a safe and enjoyable experience

Special Offer/Incentive:
A 10% discount will be applied. Please quote DE06 when booking. Cannot be combined with any other discount or promotional offer.

Experiences:

Trial Lessons:
Treat your friends and family to a trial lesson in our two seat Cessna 150 or four seat Cessna 172. An ideal gift for Christmas, birthdays or that special occasion.

Trial flights last either 30 minutes, 45 minutes or one hour.

We also offer trial flights in our Robinson R22 helicopter.

Or you can combine the two – 30 minutes in a Cessna 150 and 30 minutes in a Robinson R22.

The person receiving the lesson will have a pre-flight briefing and hands-on control of the aircraft from just after take-off to just before touchdown.

On application you will be supplied with a trial lesson card and after your flight you will be presented with a certificate as a keepsake.

Balloons Over Britain

Experience the awesome thrill and peaceful serenity of hot air ballooning. We offer hot air balloon rides from more than 70 launch sites throughout the UK.

From London to Scotland, the South West of England and Wales to the Wash – we provide the most comprehensive national balloon flights network in the UK.

Experiences:

The Balloons Over Britain Gift Voucher Range

This is the most comprehensive choice of hot air balloon flight adventures across the UK. We have the widest selection of launch sites with flights regularly scheduled covering England, Scotland and Wales. Our Balloon Flight Package contains a gift voucher and is a great present for a relative, a friend, a member of staff or a valued customer.

Each voucher provides you with a wonderful ballooning experience that includes:

- Approximately one hour of flying time with full pilot briefing
- Invitation to assist with the inflation and deflation of the balloon
- Traditional ballooning champagne toast
- Merchandise presentation
- Personalised commemorative flight certificate signed by the pilot
- Return to meeting point/launch site
- The experience will last between three and four hours
- Optional in-flight photo available (in most areas)

Activity Location:
Nationwide

Contact Details:
Balloons Over Britain
T: 01404 822489
E: info@balloonsoverbritain.com
W: www.balloonsoverbritain.com

Availability:
Main Flying season March to October

Gift Vouchers:
Available – please contact us for more information

Practical Information:
Children must be at least 8 years old and over 4ft 6in high (1.4 m). A child under the age of 16 years will only be flown if accompanied by a responsible adult appointed by the parent(s) or guardian
In the interests of safety and operational requirements we cannot undertake the carriage of passengers whose declared weight exceeds 18 stone (114 kg)

Special Offer/Incentive:
A 10% discount is available – visit www.balloonsoverbritain.com and type Direct Experiences into the special offer code box.

★ **10% DISCOUNT** (see text)
Special offer code: Direct Experiences

Cabair

Cabair has Europe's largest independent group of flying schools. We offer an unrivalled range of services including aeroplane and helicopter tuition – from introductory lessons to gaining a Commercial Pilot's Licence at our two renowned Commercial Training facilities. Qualified pilots are able to self-fly hire a range of our fleet, or indeed, purchase an aircraft.

Activity Location:
Central London and South East

Contact Details:
The Cabair Group Ltd
T: 0208 236 2400
E: group@cabair.com
W: www.flyingvouchers.com

Practical Information:
All vouchers are valid for six months from the date of issue and are non-refundable

Experiences:

Introductory Flights:
Realise your own ambition or make a superb gift of the experience to a loved one with our attractive flight vouchers which may be used at any of Cabair's PPL schools located at Biggin Hill, Blackbushe, Cranfield, Denham, Elstree and Rochester.

Our attractive flight vouchers are supplied in smart presentation packs and on completion of your first flight, you will *receive a First Flight Certificate* as a reminder of a fabulous flight!

We offer three introductory flight packages:

- The Singleton (30 minutes)
- The Land Away Double (1 hour)
- The Flying Start (5 hours)

All include a pre-flight briefing, fantastic 'hands-on flight' and count towards your Private Pilot's Licence.

Delta Aviation

The UK's leading flying experience operator founded in 1993. Flying from over 17 locations nationwide, Delta owns and operates the world's largest fleet of vintage Tiger Moth biplane aircraft as well as offering a number of flying experiences in other exciting aircraft. Each flying experience provides a unique and exhilarating, once in a lifetime adventure.

Experiences:

- *Try the Tiger Moth.* Take to the skies in one of Britain's most famous aircraft – the Tiger Moth. Your flight will last 15 minutes and is available from three nationwide locations
- *Introduction to Aerobatics.* Fly your own aerobatics sequence in an aerobatic aircraft. Your flight will last 20–25 minutes and operate from nationwide locations
- *Tame the Tiger Moth.* Chocks away – absorb the magnificent views from the open cockpit as you fly over the rolling British countryside with the wind in your hair. Your flight will last 30 minutes and operates from nationwide locations
- *Ultimate Aerobatics.* Take to the skies in the CAP10 or Pitts Special – ultimate aerobatics aircraft. Your flight will last 25 minutes and operates from locations nationwide
- *Warbird Experience.* This really is a rare opportunity to relish first hand the thrill and excitement of flying in a T-6, the famous World War II classic fighter-trainer aircraft. Various flight durations available from 20 to 60 minutes from two locations

Activity Location:
Experiences operate from locations nationwide. For latest locations please visit our website

Contact Details:
Delta Aviation
T: 01223 874346
E: admin@deltaaviation.co.uk
W: www.deltaaviation.co.uk

Practical Information:
You should be agile. Max. weight 18 stone, max. height 6 ft 4 in. May not be suitable for anyone with a known medical condition

Equipment:
You will be loaned a helmet, headset and flying jacket (dependent on aircraft type)

Availability:
Flights mainly operate from April–September with some limited availability during winter months. All flights are weather dependent

Gift vouchers:
You will receive an open-dated voucher which is valid for 12 months from the date of purchase

Corporate:
Tailored to your requirements – call for further details

Special Offer/Incentive:
Please quote UGE06 to receive 10% off your flying experience with Delta Aviation. Cannot be used in conjunction with any other offers or promotions.

★ 10% DISCOUNT
When you quote REF: UGE06

Fly CB

Many people dream of learning to fly. Fly CB provides flying instruction and pilot training in high quality, fully maintained new generation microlight aircraft. Learning to fly can be a life-changing process, so why not book a trial flight today and take the first step towards your pilot's licence.

Activity Location:
East Midlands, East Anglia and South East

Contact Details:
FlyCB
T: 0870 850 4868
E: info@flycb.com
W: www.flycb.com

Availability:
Booking is essential. Please call 0870 850 4868 or visit www.flycb.com

Practical Information:
Authority from a parent or guardian is required for those under 17 years of age. Solo flying cannot be undertaken until a student is 16 years of age
The weight limit is 95kgs

Experiences:

Trial Flying Lessons:
20 minutes, 30 minutes or 60 minutes. Trial lessons provide a brief introduction to the magic of flight and an opportunity for you to take the controls under the supervision of an instructor.

Landaway special
For something a bit different, enjoy a return trip to a local airfield. Listen and learn on the way there and put it into practice on the way back. (Approx. 90 mins flying time.)

Trial lessons include gift voucher, 10 minutes pre-flight brief and a gift certificate.

Training Packages:

- *5-Hour Course.* Want to experience a little more? Then this course is for you. Includes 5 hours of dual instruction and club membership
- *25-Hour Course.* The full minimum required hours flying course, including 25 hours dual instruction, NPPL (M) course books, equipment and flight bag
- *Corporate/Club Flying Days.* A fun and memorable experience:
  - Groups of up to 30 people
  - Includes a barbeque lunch/supper and drinks
  - A light-hearted talk on flying followed by a 20 or 30 minute trial flight
  - All participants receive a souvenir certificate
- *Team Building Experience Days.* An airborne orienteering event that encourages teamwork, problem solving, planning, time management and observational skills – as well as being great fun!
- *Incentive Voucher Scheme.* Incentivise staff or valued customers by offering them the chance to experience the thrill of flight

Microlight Sport Aviation Ltd

Provider of the best personalised flight training on microlight aircraft as well as sales and service of aircraft, engines and instruments since 1990.

Mr Deepak Mahajan, director, flight instructor and examiner, has been teaching people to fly for over 16 years.

Activity Location:
Central London

Contact Details:
Microlight Sport Aviation Ltd
T: 020 8325 0197/01708 558 740
E: info@microlightsport.co.uk
W: www.microlightsport.co.uk

Practical Information:
Full time UK CAA approved instructors
Open cockpit and closed cockpit microlight aircraft

Availability:
Open throughout the year

Vouchers:
All vouchers are valid for one year from date of purchase

Experiences:

Courses available include:

- Trial flight in a microlight aircraft (30 minutes and 60 minutes)
- Half day course
- One day course
- Complete flight training course to gain licence on microlight aircraft

When you arrive at the airfield, you will be made welcome and registered with your voucher and identification documents. You will be briefed by your flight instructor and you may take control of the aircraft right from the start, if conditions allow. Alternatively, you may choose to enjoy the flight and let the instructor take you around for an aerial tour.

You may choose to order a video movie of your flight; for an extra charge, we will edit and present you with a permanent record of your thrilling day.

Arrows Experience at Thruxton Motorsport Centre

Can you imagine performing close formation aerobatics with former Red Arrow pilots? Now you can. Jump on board the Pitts special aircraft and get ready for the flight of your life. This is extreme and probably the most exhilarating experience available to the general public. If you're looking for something different or the ultimate adrenalin buzz – look no further!

Activity Location:
South West

Contact Details:
Thruxton Motorsport Centre
T: 01264 882222
E: info@thruxtonracing.co.uk
W: www.thruxtonracing.co.uk

Practical Information:
Min. height 5ft
Max. height 6ft 4in
Max. weight 15 stone
Min. age 17
Participants need to fully understand the safety briefing, to understand and be able to communicate with the pilot via the intercom and/or hand signals whilst in the plane and be able to exit the cockpit unaided

Equipment:
All safety equipment will be provided, including helmets, gloves and flight suit

Availability:
Experiences are available on selected weekends from March to October

Gift packs and vouchers:
Valid for one year from the date of purchase

Corporate events:
We operate bespoke corporate packages; please get in touch to discuss requirements

Special Offer
A 10% discount is available for the Arrows Experiences when you quote Ref. TXNAX. Cannot be combined with any other discounts or promotional offers.

★ 10% DISCOUNT
When you quote REF: TXNAX

Experiences:

Arrows Experience:
Profile of your day:

- Issue of flight suits and helmets
- Safety briefing
- Purpose of close formation aerobatics
- Red Arrows and fighters information video
- Flight details
- Call signs
- Procedures
- Meet the pilots
- Strap in
- Cockpit briefing
- Pairs formation take-off
- Close formation climb to 1000 ft. plus
- Formation high-G turns
- Loop the loops
- Barrel rolls
- Tail chasing and dog fighting

Total duration of experience 2½–3 hours. Total flying time 30 minutes.

This experience operates under an Air Operators Certificate issued by the Civil Aviation Authority and meets all operation and maintenance requirements set down for companies flying the public as passengers.

Pennine Flying School

We are a dedicated flying school who can teach you hang-gliding skills. Whether you are a novice who wants to take a taster flight or a more advanced glider, we have the safety knowledge and experts to get you in the air!

Experiences:

Taster Days:
This is a day's event that starts around 10.30am until 4.00pm. We use two sites along the M62 corridor, depending on wind direction and speed. You will experience the thrill of getting off the ground as well as gaining knowledge on rigging. The day is spent with you and the other members of the group flying whilst instructors and assistants are keeping the glider(s) secure by holding them with tethers.

Elementary Pilot Course:
This course takes a minimum of five lessons. We work our way through the training syllabus as written in the Student Training Log Book. This includes membership of The British Hang Gliding and Paragliding Association (BHPA). Once the pilot has attained the required standard and has completed all the relevant tasks, including a written exam, they will be signed off. It is at this point that the pilot can purchase his or her own glider and continue to the next stage, Club Pilot.

Courses can be completed abroad within a holiday package – thereby saving money and speeding training. Please contact us to discuss your individual requirements.

Activity Location:
North West

Contact Details:
The Pennine Flying School
T: 077920 79855
E: info@pennineflyingschool.com
W: www.pennineflyingschool.com

Equipment:
All safety and flying equipment is provided

Practical information:
All participants must be of a reasonable fitness and be anything from teenagers to pensioners

Availability:
Throughout the year but weather dependent

Gift Vouchers:
Available from £130

Recommended:
Comfortable sports clothing with strong footwear (walking boots are ideal)

Special Offers:
A 10% discount is available to readers. Please quote reference DE07 when booking. Cannot be combined with any other discounts or promotional offers.
Discounts are also available for university students. Please enquire when booking.

★ **10% DISCOUNT**
When you quote REF: DE07

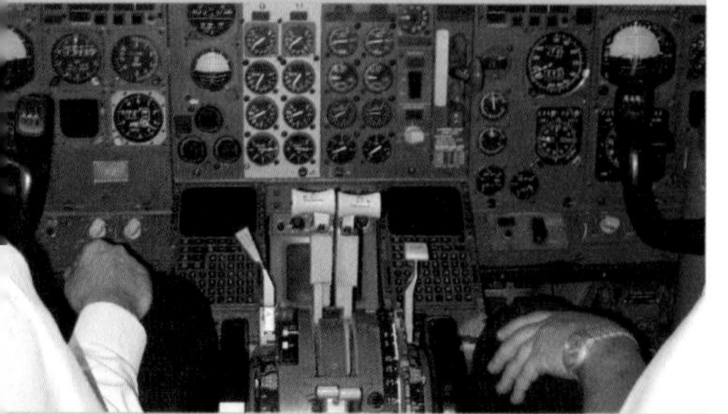

STS (Simulator Training Services)

STS (Simulator Training Services) is the preferred organisation for those who seek the highest level of competence, professionalism and excellent test results in JAA instrument flight training.

Activity Location:
South East and South West

Contact Details:
Simulator Training Services
T: 07799 887274
E: bookings@simulatortrainingservices.co.uk
W: www.simulatortrainingservices.co.uk

Practical Information:
You will need to present a valid passport or photocard driving license with you on the day. Failure will result in you being unable to participate in the experience
Min. age 16 yrs
You may take up to three guests with you to sit in the simulator while you pilot the plane

Experiences:

30-minute Solo Flight Simulator Experience:
Take the controls of a Boeing 727 or 747. This simulator has been developed for training airline pilots. It is the top-of-the-range, fully motional and is as close as you can get to flying a passenger aeroplane, without years of training. Prepare for take-off and the simulator is at your command. After the take-off scenario you will have the opportunity to fly the plane in a variety of conditions including a simulated emergency. An instructor is your co-pilot to help your read the mass of instruments and bring the plane safely into land at the end of your session.

Ultimate High

Tailored to your requirements, from extremely gentle to gently extreme! Ultimate High operates a fleet of ex-military and aerobatic aircraft, flown by ex-Red Arrows and military combat trained instructors.

Based at the former home of the Red Arrows and operated as part of our advanced flying training school, we bring a totally new level of military style organisation, excitement and professionalism to aviation experiences.

Experiences:

Top Gun Experience:
Our 'Top Gun' experience gives you the chance to be part of an air combat team and actually fly missions! With an instructor you'll experience extreme aerobatics, close formation flying and 'Top Gun' style tailchasing – then take the controls to do it all yourself!

Profile of your day:

- Welcome and kit out into flying suits
- Pre-flight briefing
- Students are matched into 'Top Gun' pairs
- Flight:
  - formation take-off (2 aircraft)
  - formation close manoeuvring in the climb
  - demonstration and practice of effects of controls and aerobatic manoeuvres
  - hands-on stick time – opportunity for you to fly some aerobatics yourself
  - demonstration and practice of tail-chase with another aeroplane
  - return to base
- Debrief and receive signed flight certificate

Activity Location:
South West

Contact Details:
Ultimate High
T: 01243 576137
E: info@ultimatehigh.co.uk
W: www.ultimatehigh.co.uk

Practical Information:
Flights are approx. 40 minutes long although you should expect to be with us 3–4 hours
All flying is subject to weather, aircraft serviceability, pilot rosters and airfield availability. It is essential to call on the day
You are required to complete a Medical Self Certification form before flying with us
If you are over 55, as a formality, we require a letter from your doctor confirming your suitability to fly with us
The weight limit in the Extra 300 aircraft is 16 stone and 20 stone in the Bulldog

Availability:
Flights operate March–October, except on Sundays

Special Offer/Incentive:
20% off if you book as a pair.

★ **20% DISCOUNT**
If you book as a pair

Airborne

Inject a large dose of excitement into someone's special day with a gift voucher for a paragliding course! An ideal gift for the adventure enthusiast, or a perfect surprise for the couch potato!! Just choose the course you'd like to buy and we'll send you a gift voucher to present on the big day. You don't have to book the exact dates; the recipient just has to let us know a minimum of two weeks before they would like to come to confirm availability.

Activity Location:
North East and North West

Contact Details:
Airborne
T: 08701 998 976/0709 200 9133
E: info@airborne.uk.com
W: www.airborne.uk.com

Practical Information:
Max. weight 18 stone/115 kg
Min. age 15 years

Availability:
We operate in the UK from April until mid December

Special Offer/Incentive:
Reserve two places – second place for *half price*! Quote UGE/06 to qualify.

Experiences:

Tandem Flight:
You will be given a minimum of 15 minutes tandem flying with the UK Champion. You will be shown basic safety elements and once airborne you can sit back and relax!

One-Day Taster Course:
Typically by the end of the day you will have flown from 20 metres. Some individuals manage to fly from as high as 100 metres, but will depend on natural ability, fitness and pre-course study (we have a pre-course training video available).

Two-Day Taster Course:
The first day is exactly the same as the fun day above. On the second day you will pick up from where you left off on day one – continuing your short flights which, depending on your skill level will increase gradually in altitude to up to 300 ft.

★ **50% DISCOUNT** on second place when you quote REF: UGE/06

Cambridge Gliding Centre

The premier gliding site for Eastern England hosts Cambridge Gliding Club. Facilities include a 100-acre airfield, a large fleet of gliders, aerotow and winch launching.

Cambridge Gliding Club is a member of the British Gliding Association and all instructors are trained to BGA regulations.

The centre operates with a mixture of paid staff and volunteers; professional instructors and winch drivers are employed throughout the summer.

Activity Location:
South East

Contact Details:
Cambridge Gliding Centre
T: 01767 677077
E: office@glide.co.uk
W: www.glide.co.uk

Practical Information:
Some things that would prevent you from attending a course:

- You are under 12 yrs old
- You weigh over 109 kg (240 lbs)
- You are subject to sudden disabling health attacks such as epilepsy

Availability:
The centre is open seven days a week from April to September and four days a week from October to March
Booking is essential

Experiences:

We provide two ways of getting airborne. You can either be launched by a winch or towed up behind a light aircraft. Both offer a fantastic experience. Once you are airborne your instructor will demonstrate the use of the controls and show you how a glider flies. You will be encouraged to handle the controls as much as possible during the flight.

Aerotow 2000

Aerotow to 2000 feet and up to 30 minutes flying. Handle the controls or just enjoy the experience.

Aerotow 3000

Aerotow to 3000 feet and up to 40 minutes flying.

Each of the above flights can be taken at weekends throughout the year and on weekdays during our summer season from April to September.

Introductory Course

Three aerotows to 2000 feet and initial instruction – this forms part of the BGA syllabus.

Because the club is busy at weekends introductory courses are only run Monday to Friday.

Western Air (Thruxton) Ltd

If learning or wanting to learn to fly, there are few places which can offer the expertise, facilities and history of Thruxton. All training at Western Air is carried out over the beautiful Hampshire and Wiltshire countryside. Our base at Thruxton Airfield offers a wide range of facilities, for all pilots whether trainees or those with years of experience.

Activity Location:
South West

Contact details:
Western Air (Thruxton) Ltd
T: 01264 773900
E: westernair@thruxtonairport.com
W: www.westernairthruxton.co.uk

Gift Vouchers:
Gift Vouchers available, the amount of the voucher determines the time spent flying

Experiences:

Trial lessons:
A trial flight enables you to take control of the aircraft in the capable hands of one of our instructors and maybe even land the aircraft. If you live locally you can fly over familiar countryside and see it from a completely different perspective, otherwise enjoy the beautiful Hampshire and Wiltshire landscape from the sky.

Other Courses:

- *JAR Private Pilot's Licence (PPL)*: Instructors will personally guide you through 45 hours of flight training of which 10 hours will be flying on your own. Resident instructors and examiners guide you through and conduct all tests both flying and written at Thruxton. The PPL allows you to fly around the UK and in any country within the EU

After the PPL has been completed, the following advanced courses are available:

- National Pilot's Licence
- Multi-Engine Piston Licence
- Tail Wheel conversion
- Radio Telephony course
- Aerobatics
- Night Rating

Stratford on Avon Gliding Club

Experience the thrill of near silent flight over the beautiful Warwickshire countryside and learn to fly a modern glider with a fully qualified instructor.

Experiences:

Trial Lesson Gift Voucher:
Entitles the holder to a single glider flight - an ideal way for anyone to experience gliding for the first time and get 'hands-on' the controls.

One-Day Course Voucher:
The holder will experience up to five flights (or 75 minutes in the air) - perfect for anyone wishing to get a head start in learning to fly.

Five-Day Course:
A whole week learning to fly a glider! Intensive training that will yield fantastic progress towards your first solo flight.

Evening Flying Events:
For between 10 and 20 people wishing to experience a glider flight - ideal for company social events. Events can be booked May through to early September

Activity Location:
Midlands

Contact Details:
Stratford on Avon Gliding Club
T: 01789 731095 club house
T: 01789 266502 vouchers/courses
E: enquiries@stratfordgliding.co.uk
W: www.stratfordgliding.co.uk

Practical Information:
To fly, you must be:

- Aged 13 or older
- Between 145 cm and 193 cm tall (4 ft 9 in to 6 ft 4 in)
- Weigh between 45 kg and 102 kg (7–16 stone)

Availability:
Open 7 days from 1 May to first week of September
Open Thursday, Saturday and Sunday rest of year

Special Offer/Incentive:
A 10% discount for all bookings via Direct Experiences - please quote ref SDE2006 when contacting us. Cannot be used in conjunction with any other offers or promotions.

★ 10% DISCOUNT
When you quote REF: SDE2006

Kids

'When you're curious, you find lots of interesting things to do.'

WALT DISNEY

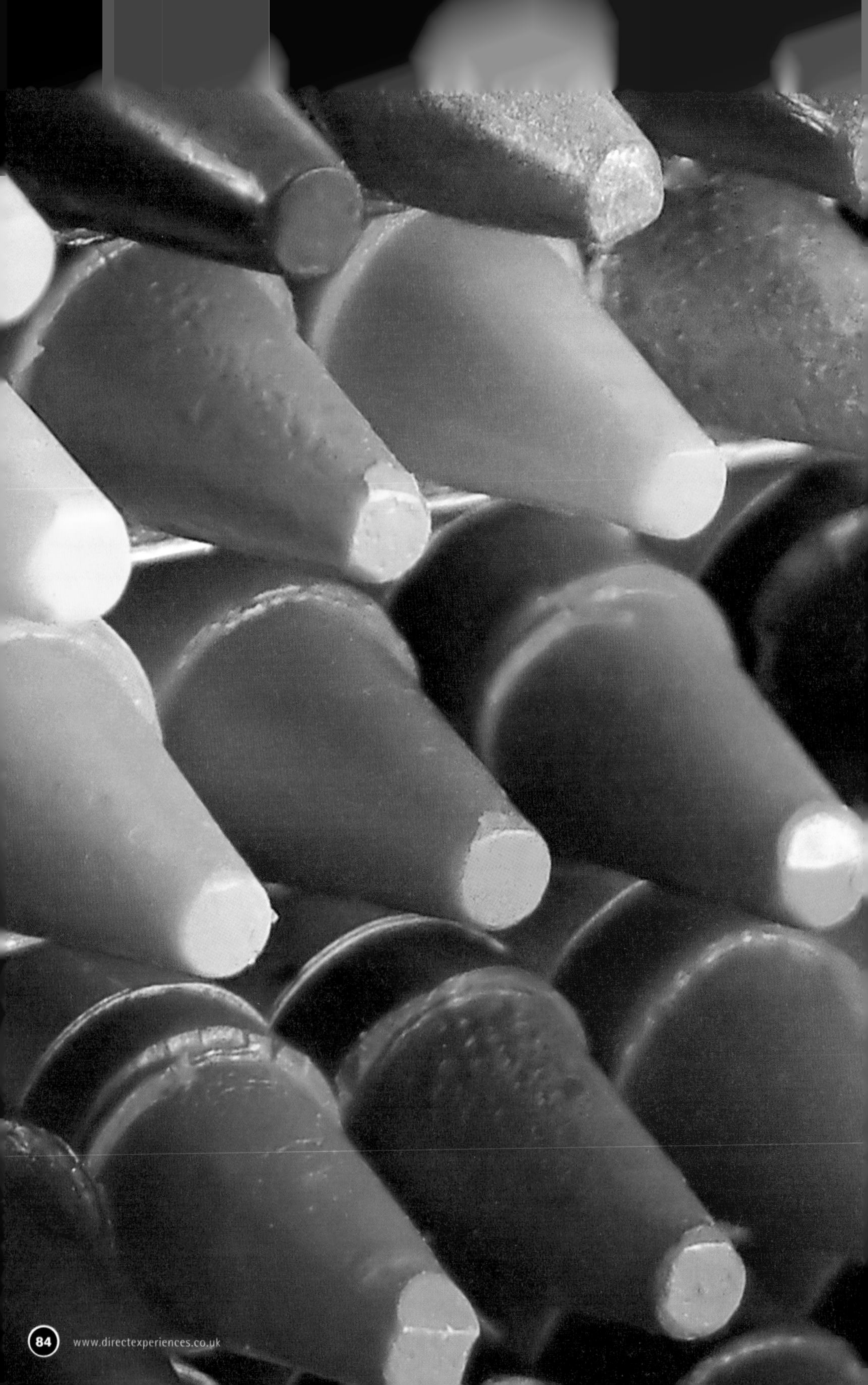

Kids stuff

In my day you could entertain kids by giving them a small block of wood or two tin cans and a length of string. Now it seems most of them own more electronics than Jodrell bank and would no more entertain themselves playing marbles than I would.

Lucky kids. But bad news for parents who can struggle a bit to get their offspring out of the house and doing something a bit different. Which is what the pros are there for. Because personal entertainment systems are all very well, but when it comes to dreaming big the kids need to get out into the big wide world.

Your mission

One thing that hasn't changed over the last few generations is the appeal of spy adventure. These days they're as likely to dream of being Jinx as James Bond but the basics are the same – good clean wholesome fun. So I wasn't too surprised to learn that there are Spy Camps for kids.

The only thing that troubled me was that I've come across Spy Camps before and they majored on such essential skills as axe throwing, evasive driving, and the handling and firing of semi-automatic weapons. Must-have life skills undoubtedly, but most adolescents seem to have enough capacity to wreak havoc without actually being introduced to the wonders of assault rifles and Semtex.

The good news is that the junior versions of these camps stop slightly short of live rounds and real cars. Instead there are any number of sneaky low-down tricks on offer, including operating hidden cameras, planting and monitoring bugs and listening in on radio equipment. I'm not sure that the average 11-year-old hasn't already got most of this technology but at least they get to use it right and prepare for a career in MI6.

There's a quick-draw competition and shoot-out of course, but kids get to use laser tag guns, which are considerably less dangerous than anything they can get their hands on at home. Plus they get to dodge laser beams, crack codes and deactivate bombs in true *Mission Impossible* style. When I was between 10 and 16 that would have been pretty much my definition of heaven. But what do I know – I was the one kept happy with lumps of wood and baked bean cans.

Swinging from tree to tree

When I was young I used to love climbing trees. Things haven't changed much and today's kids still love climbing, but now they can take it to the next level. Instead of just looking for a handy oak in the local park, today's kids can climb to fantastic heights in specially designed climbing parks. These parks also have the advantage for parents of supplying enough ropes, harnesses and instructors for you to be assured that your simian offspring are safe at all times. Most places will insist that at least one adult accompanies the children, so big kids will also get the chance to swing through the trees.

Outdoors types

Most children are bursting with energy and it's often a challenge to find enough for them to do to run off all their liveliness. Sporting activities that today's children can get involved in include surfing, sailing, wakeboarding, windsurfing, water skiing, raft building, orienteering and rock climbing. Take them for a day out with one of the suppliers listed in the next section and by the end of the day they should be ready to fall asleep before you even get home. Giving you the chance to have the evening to yourself, put your feet up and enjoy a bit of peace and quiet.

Spy Games

Spy Games have taken the best action and adventure from the world of secret agents and designed a range of events and activities that allow anyone to experience for themselves.

Our fully qualified staff will let kids play at being a secret agent, with climbing, shooting laser combat games, zip line, booby trap dodging, code cracking, map and flag identification, an overnight survival camp out and various other spy missions. Through these fun activities, kids learn the valuable skills of teamwork and problem solving, as they make new friends and develop the personal attributes of self-confidence and self-discipline.

Activity Location:
North West, Midlands and South East

Contact Details:
Spy Games Ltd
T: 0845 1303 007
E: info@spy-games.com
W: www.spy-games.com

Practical Information:
Our staff are qualified and experienced youth activity supervisors with backgrounds in education, military, law enforcement and social services

Special Offers:
A 10% discount is available to readers. Please mention Direct Experiences when booking. Cannot be combined with any other special offers, discount or promotion.

Experiences:

Spy Camp Experience:
The ultimate experience for any young secret agent.

Spy Games have created the Spy Camp Experience for children aged between 10 and 16.

They will take part in a variety of secret agent training such as learning how to operate hidden cameras, bugging devices and radio equipment. Take part in a shoot-out using our completely harmless state-of-the-art laser tag guns; dodge laser beams to crack open the safe against the clock; learn how to quick draw their pistol from a holster and finally crack codes to deactivate the bomb as the clock ticks away!

★ **10% DISCOUNT**
Please mention Direct Experiences when booking

WakeMK

Waterskiing and wakeboarding has been around for ages, but over the last three years wakeboarding has become the fastest-growing water sport activity in the country. With the advancement of cable ski facilities the cost of participating has been greatly reduced and this has opened the doors to people of all ages and abilities. This high speed, adrenaline-filled sport is guaranteed to put a smile on your face.

WakeMK is one of the best places to learn. Our team of friendly professional instructors are dedicated to helping you improve.

Activity Location:
South East

Contact Details:
Wake MK
T: 0870 748 3030
E: info@wakemk.com
W: www.wakemk.com

Availability:
We recommend pre-booking as places are strictly limited

Practical Information:
Min. age 8 yrs
Weight less than 19 stone
Must be able to swim 50m
Parents can watch from the dock or take a welcome break at our new indoor restaurant overlooking the cable lake

Recommended:
Bring swim shorts and a towel

Gift Vouchers:
Available from £25 to £600

Special Offer:
A 10% discount is available to readers. Please mention Direct Experiences when booking. Cannot be combined with any other special offers, discounts or promotions.

★ 10% DISCOUNT
Please mention Direct Experiences when booking

Experiences:

Junior Sessions:
We run special junior sessions from 1pm to 3pm every weekday during every school holiday. We'll teach you how to wakeboard and get you started with your first tricks. We provide all the kit you need including: a wetsuit to keep you warm, buoyancy aids, helmets and of course wakeboards. You will start by learning some basic safety and we'll teach you about your equipment. Each course is run by an experienced instructor and rider who will teach you all you need to know over those first three sessions.

- We have installed a brand new cable this year with easier and smoother corners for beginners – that means the corners are easier, you'll progress faster and you'll get more time riding
- We run the cable at a slower speed – making it easier to get up and started
- We run a taxi boat service – so if you fall we'll pick you up and drop you back at the start dock
- We keep a record of your progress with your own personal card – your instructor will mark off your achievements as you progress and help you strive for the next level

Hydro Extreme Action Sports

It's so important for children to experience a range of activities to give their different qualities a chance to shine. Action sports are an excellent outlet for life's modern-day teenager, physically and emotionally. Qualities gained are personal development and working as part of a team in a non-competitive environment.

Activity Location:
Midlands

Contact Details:
Hydro Extreme Action Sports Park
T: 01905 620044
E: info@hydroextreme.com
W: www.hydroextreme.com

Practical Information:
If clients are unable to swim 25 metres, the chief instructor must be notified prior to the course
Anyone suffering from any medical conditions must notify Hydro Extreme prior to booking and again on arrival at the centre. The Company can accept no responsibility for any clients' medical condition

Availability:
All courses or personal coaching are available 7 days a week. Please phone 01905 620044 for more details.

Experiences:

Sailing – Taster Session:
Sailing is one of the longest surviving water sports in history and it's still as popular as ever! It's just so versatile, from small dinghys to 50-ft yachts, the principles are the same. You can be part of a crew or sail solo, whichever you prefer. It can be relaxing, exhilarating or non-stop adrenaline action; get on board – sailing is here to stay!

In just three hours after being a complete beginner you will be able to sail across the lake unassisted, tack and return. You will have knowledge of safety aspects and basic equipment terminology, which will give you the confidence to practice further.

Windsurfing:
One of the best ways to introduce children to the excitement of the water world. By staying reasonably(!) dry, kids build their water confidence while learning new skills.

In just three hours we will take you from complete beginner level and teach you the basics of windsurfing using the right equipment. You will be able to windsurf across the lake, turn around and return to your starting point. You will also learn to sail upwind.

Rockingham Motor Speedway

In just five years Rockingham has become more than just a motor sport facility. It has become one of the top entertainment venues in the Midlands and the UK.

Activity Location:
Midlands

Contact Details:
The Race School Rockingham
T: 01536 271272
E: experiences@rockingham.co.uk
W: www.rockingham.co.uk

Practical Information:
Crash helmets will be provided.
Participants and a parent are required to sign a disclaimer before taking part. An adult must accompany children

Availability:
Operational from February to November, 1-2 days per month, normally on a Saturday

Gift Vouchers:
Gift vouchers can be purchased for an experience, which are valid for 12 months

Experiences:

First Drive:
It's your first time in the driver's seat and you're driving on the private roads around Rockingham. You're within touching distance of the UK's fastest race circuit and it's you behind the wheel. You concentrate hard; focus on the road ahead, your instructor guiding you all the while. This is so good so incredible. And when it finally ends, you're filled with thoughts of your own car, your own independence. Soon you'll be old enough, very soon. But for now you just smile. The best present you ever had? Oh yes.

Even youngsters can discover the thrill of driving at Rockingham. Here, young people from 12 to 16 years old can get behind a steering wheel for the first time in safe, controlled conditions with an ADI instructor who will teach them the rudiments of driving. This experience is all about helping young learners to make the most of that crucial first drive – to learn more, to experience more and to have much more fun too.

Outdoor Adventure

Outdoor Adventure was established 25 years ago as a small activity centre; we remain small which enables us to deliver high-quality programmes and holidays and a very personal experience. This ethos promotes a fun and relaxed atmosphere that benefits everyone and makes it possible to provide consistent quality assurance and value for money.

Activity location:
South West

Contact Details:
Outdoor Adventure
T: 01288 362900
E: info@outdooradventure.co.uk
W: www.outdooradventure.co.uk

Practical Information:
Equipment is available on site

Availability:
Open Easter to October 7 days per week

Special Offer/Incentive:
A 10% discount is available to readers. Please mention Direct Experiences when booking. Cannot be combined with any other special offer, discount or promotion.

Experiences:

OA Surf School:
The OA Surf School has it all! Surf, food, accommodation, instruction, the latest equipment, local transport and great evenings.

Our local beaches pick up the best of any swell arriving in the South-West – the surf is the same as Newquay but without the crowds! Widemouth Bay has ideal waves for learning or improving your surfing. The water is clean and Widemouth Bay has a Blue Flag Award. We have four beaches within a short drive, giving us a variety of different swell sizes, wind direction and stages of tide.

Family Fun:
Family adventure starts here. We have a full range of activities to suit everyone. These include bodyboarding, windsurfing, coasteering, climbing, abseiling and coastal walking, to name but a few. Whether you all want to join in the same activity or pursue different ones, we'll even be flexible and do whatever the weather predicts would be best.

★ **10% DISCOUNT** Please mention Direct Experiences when booking

Go Ape! High Wire Forest Adventure

Spend a memorable three hours trekking from tree to tree via an assortment of rope bridges, Tarzan swings and zip slides up to 60 feet above the forest floor. Courses are split into five or six separate zones with exhilarating zip slides bringing you back to Earth at the end of each section.

Activity location:
There are seven courses around the UK in 2006. Five more planned for 2007. Check www.goape.co.uk for details

Contact Details:
Go Ape!
T: 0870 444 5562
E: info@goape.co.uk
W: www.goape.co.uk

Practical Information:
Min. age 10 years; Min. height 1.4 m
Under 18 year olds must be accompanied by a participating adult. One adult can supervise five under 18 year olds (but only two can be under 16 years)

Equipment:
All safety equipment is provided

Recommended:
Comfortable clothing and enclosed footwear. No sandals or flip flops

Availability:
Daily from end of March to end of October; weekends in November

Corporate Events:
Customised corporate packages are available, which can include conference facilities, mountain biking and BBQs

Gift vouchers:
Available via the booking centre or website

Special Offer/Incentive:
We're offering a 10% discount in 2007 (excluding corporate packages). Call 0870 444 5562 quoting *Ultimate Gift Experiences*. Cannot be combined with any other special offers, discounts or promotions.

★ **10% DISCOUNT** Please mention *Ultimate Gift Experiences* when booking

Experiences:

- *Sherwood Forest, Nottingham.* Swing through the trees and speed down zip slides. Also enjoy Go Ape's only treetop-to-treetop zip wires
- *Grizedale Forest, Cumbria.* King of the Swingers! Rope bridges, a Tarzan swing and zip slides stretch through the forest up to 60 feet above the forest floor, the highest of any Go Ape course
- *Delamere Forest, Cheshire.* This course boasts the longest zip slide of any Go Ape adventure, over 200 metres long
- *Thetford Forest, East Anglia.* The first Go Ape course to open contains many challenges, new and old, which keep customers coming back
- *Forest of Dean, Gloucestershire.* The course consists of some 35 obstacles winding though the treetops set against a stunning forest and lake backdrop
- *Swinley Forest, Bracknell, Berkshire.* The usual challenging rope bridges, thrilling Tarzan swing and zip slides await you, as does a friendly welcome from our attentive staff, who will ensure you're not hugging too many trees!
- *Moors Valley, Nr. Ringwood, Dorset.* Yet another stunning course with various rope bridges, Tarzan swings and zip slides

Haven Banks Outdoor Education Centre

Haven Banks Outdoor Education Centre is situated in Exeter on the canal and specialises in activity-based courses for all ages and abilities. The centre is approved by BCU and RYA. Activities offered include canoeing, sailing, windsurfing, caving, climbing and orienteering. Raft building and problem solving are other popular pursuits.

Experiences:

We have a whole variety of events to choose from and day, weekend or week courses can be tailor-made to your requirements.

Activities on offer:
Kayaking, canoeing, sailing, windsurfing, raft building, environmental education, team challenge, climbing wall, orienteering, rock climbing, caving and key skills induction programmes.

Courses on offer:
Taster sessions, week-long multi-activity breaks, school, youth and adult groups, children's summer holiday play scheme, adult evening courses, key and core skills development and instructor training courses.

Facilities:
The centre has purpose-converted waterfront premises with heated changing rooms, showers, a classroom, extensive stores and outside areas. It has over 70 canoes and kayaks, 18 sailing boats, 10 windsurfers, safety boats, climbing kits, a permanent orienteering course on the adjacent country park, an on-site climbing wall and environmental studies equipment.

So whether you're on holiday in the area or live close by, why not get in touch with us and get busy with us?

Activity Location:
South West

Contact Details:
Haven Banks Outdoor Education Centre
T: 01392 434668
E: havenb@devon.gov.uk
W: www.devon.gov.uk/haven_banks_oec

Practical Information:
All safety equipment is provided and all our staff are professionally fully qualified

Availability:
Open year round
Group or individual bookings welcome

Special Offer/Incentive:
A 10% discount is available to readers. Cannot be used in conjunction with any other discounts or promotional offers.

★ **10% DISCOUNT** Please mention *Ultimate Gift Experiences* when booking

Brookbank Canoes & Kayaks

We run a wide range of courses and trips for all levels of paddler. Our experienced and qualified coaches will ensure you have a safe and enjoyable time whilst learning in a positive and friendly atmosphere.

Activity Location:
North West and Scotland
Holidays available throughout the UK and abroad

Contact Details:
Brookbank Canoes & Kayaks
T: 0161 474 1499
E: info@brookbankcanoes.co.uk
W: www.brookbankcanoes.co.uk

Availability:
Open throughout the year

Corporates:
Tailor-made group bookings available on request

Special Offer/Incentive:
Please quote *Ultimate Gift Experiences* when booking your course for special offers.

Experiences:

Flat Water Kayaking:
Aimed at the complete beginner looking to start out in the sport or as a useful refresher for those who may have kayaked in the dim and distant past.

White Water Kayaking:
This is aimed at paddlers who can handle kayaks confidently on flat water and wish to try their hand at running a river. You will learn how to read the water in order to navigate rapids successfully and perform skills and techniques including ferry gliding, breakouts and more.

Open Canoeing:
The Open Canoe is ideal for families looking for a fun and safe activity in which anyone can take part, for couples wanting to share an activity and for solo paddlers to explore their local waterways.

Sea Kayaking:
This gives you the chance to get away into the wilderness and get close to nature. Kayaking metres away from seals, watching sea birds as they fish – even seeing dolphins – are some of the experiences you may expect when kayaking off the beautiful coast of Anglesey.

John Nike Leisuresport Ltd

We offer fantastic value ski, snowboard, and toboggan centres in the UK. Our centres are the perfect places to experience the excitement of snow sports in a safe environment. Whether you want to learn to ski, snowboard, ice-skate or have lots of fun on our toboggans, you'll find our centres offer the very best facilities for you and your friends.

Experiences:

Swadlincote Ski and Snowboard Centre (Midlands):
We offer lessons and fun sessions in skiing, snowboarding, blading, fun activity days, tobogganing and sno-tubing.

Llandudno Ski & Snowboard Centre:
For skiing, snowboarding, tobogganing, sno-tubing or alpine adventure golf, we are the place to be.

Bristol Ice Rink:
We offer public sessions for all types of skaters including a full Learn to Skate Programme and a Junior Ice Hockey Programme.

Plymouth Ski Centre:
From lessons to open practice, Plymouth Ski Centre offers a wide variety of activities for skiers, snowboarders and bladers, sno-tubers and tobogganers.

Bracknell Ski & Snowboard Centre:
We offer a whole range of activities; skiing, boarding and blade lessons, along with specialised sessions with Alpine and Junior Ski Clubs, Snowboard and Freestyle Nights, Instructor and Race Training.

Chatham Dry Ski Slope:
The centre is open throughout the year and offers skiers, snowboarders, and bladers of all levels the facilities to practice and learn new skills. Tobogganing and sno-tubing are also available for great family fun.

Locations:
Midlands, Wales, South West, South East

Contact Details:
Swadlincote Ski and Snowboard Centre, Derbyshire
www.swadlincoteskislope.co.uk
Tel: 01283 217200

Llandudno Ski & Snowboard Centre
www.llandudnoskislope.co.uk
Tel: 01492 874707

Plymouth Ski Centre
www.plymouthskislope.co.uk
Tel: 01752 600220

Bristol Ice Rink
www.jnll.co.uk/bristol.php
Tel: 01179 292148

Bracknell Ski and Snowboard Centre, Berkshire
www.bracknellskislope.co.uk
Tel: 01344 789000

Chatham Dry Ski Slope, Kent
www.chathamskislope.co.uk
Tel: 01634827979
Contact www.jnll.co.uk

Head Office: 01344 789000

Practical information:
Children's activities available from 4 yrs depending on the centre. Please see website for full details
Opening days and times vary for each location

Special Offer/Incentive:
A 10% discount is available to readers. Cannot be combined with any other promotion, special offer or discount.

★ **10% DISCOUNT** Please mention *Ultimate Gift Experiences* when booking

Relaxation

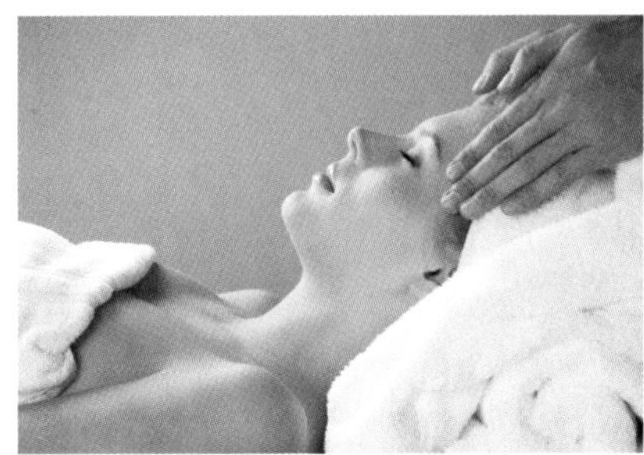

'The time to relax is when you don't have time for it.'

SYDNEY J. HARRIS, AMERICAN JOURNALIST

Take it easy

The majority of special gift experiences focus on excitement and adrenaline, but not everybody feels the need for speed and it could be a very different change of pace that hits the spot.

Spas are heaven on earth. Which is perhaps why they're popping up all over the place like Starbucks on a high street. Day spas offer serious pampering for the time and cash strapped – but your time there is precious so make sure you make the most of it. Give them a call before you arrive and check that every little detail is provided. Do you need your own robes or are they laid on? Is food provided? Are you sure you understand just what's involved with each therapy? Day spa experiences can include all sorts of relative exotica such as Indian head massage, aromatherapy, or reflexology. If you're going to be sealed up in a flotation tank like a leaky mausoleum then it's a good idea to be sure you're not actually claustrophobic. Or suffering from rabies.

Drawing up a list of questions and having a chat on the phone a day or two beforehand can make all the difference to your experience.

Getting the massage across

Go on, treat yourself to a massage. Yes, that does mean you blokes too. Studies have shown that deep-pressure massage stimulates the nerves that cause our levels of the stress hormones cortisol and epinephrine to go down, while the levels of two mood-regulating brain chemicals that act like the hormones serotonin and dopamine rise. Have you stepped into a beauty salon recently? There's a massage, treatment, lotion, potion or therapy for just about every beauty challenge that afflicts us. There's no denying you emerge from a salon feeling buoyant, relaxed, and slightly more gorgeous than when you went in.

One UK study found that massage can boost circulation and stimulate nerves that deliver blood to your organs. Another US study showed that deep mechanical massage really can delay the appearance of cellulite. Massage can help boost lymphatic drainage too – alleviating the fluid retention that can make you look puffy and bloated and it has been shown to decrease levels of stress hormones, which are associated with weight gain. All good reasons to invest in a regular massage treatment.

The standard day spa session is a smorgasbord of steam rooms, sauna, swimming pool, exercise classes, beauty treatments and lunch. Some may see this experience as being ever so slightly spoiled by a distinct absence of choccies and pork pies but for some inexplicable reason these are scorned by most spas. You can't have everything but you will emerge refreshed, rejuvenated, in perfect body/soul harmony, and raring to go down the pub.

Nirvana Spa

The award-winning Nirvana Spa is a magical retreat of pure healing waters. Imagine relaxing in a spa with six pure natural spring-fed pools with water clean enough to drink. Nirvana Spa provides the ultimate experience of peace and tranquillity in a day designed to restore, relax and refresh you. Senses are stimulated from the spa, full body massages and plunge pools in luxurious surroundings.

Experiences:

All packages include use of the spa facilities, a light meal and selected refreshments, robe and towel hire and a floatation session in our unique Dead Sea Floatation pool.

Prices vary for midweek day, midweek evenings and weekends.

- *Floatation Experience*. The standard package including the use of the spa facilities as described above
- *Tranquillity*. Choose from 25-minute face, body, hand or foot treatments
- Essential Escape. Choose from one of our 25-minute face or body treatments *plus* one of our 25-minute hand or foot treatments
- *Pure Serenity*. Choose from 25-minute face, body, hand or foot treatments
- *Ultimate Indulgence*. Includes a 55-minute facial, 55-minute aromatherapy massage and one of our hand or foot massages
- *Mother to Be*. Perfect for during and after pregnancy. Includes 70 minutes blissful beginnings treatment and a choice of one of our 25-minute hand or foot treatments
- *Men's Retreat*. Designed especially for him ... Includes one 25-minute face treatment and a choice of one of our 25-minute body treatments
- *Holistic Touch*. Treat your mind, body and soul. Choose from a 55-minute reflexology or aromatherapy massage and a choice of one of our 25-minute face treatments
- *Detox and Replenish*. Choose from 85-minute fruit scrub and detox wrap, or 55-minute full body mud envelope and one 25-minute face treatment

Activity Location:
South East

Contact details:
Nirvana Spa
T: 0118 9897575
E: info@nirvanaspa.co.uk
W: www.nirvanaspa.co.uk

Availability:
All experience vouchers can be purchased on-line

Practical Information:
All guests are provided with towels and robes for use during their visit
Clients must be 16 years and over
No smoking policy
Use of mobile phones prohibited
Please seek the advice of your doctor if you are within the first 12 weeks of pregnancy or have any medical conditions that we should take into account

Groups:
Maximum group size is six people on all spa experiences

Special Offer:
A 10% discount is available. Please mention Direct Experiences when booking. Cannot be combined with any other special offer, discount or promotion.

★ **10% DISCOUNT** Please mention Direct Experiences when booking

SALUS Natural Therapy Centre - Complementary Therapy

In the midst of our hectic lives, finding a time and space to relax and focus on yourself is rare.

Here at SALUS, we offer that opportunity with a range of complementary therapies in a cosy, relaxing and tranquil setting. Our focus at SALUS is your health and wellbeing and our treatment experience is tailored specifically to your health history and requirements, with experienced practitioners.

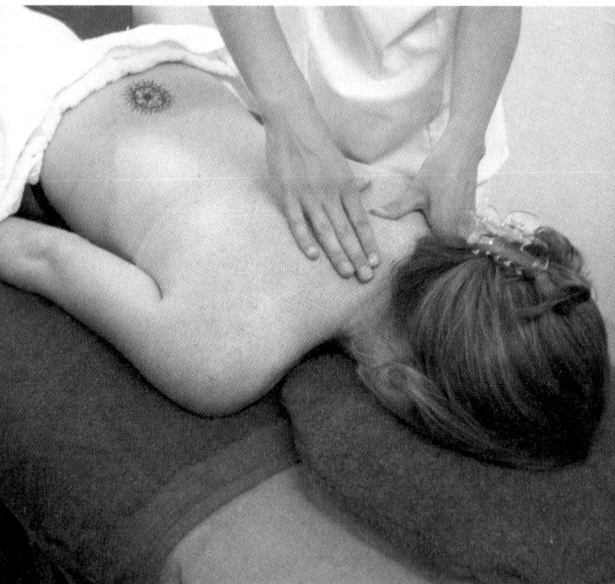

Activity Location:
Midlands

Contact Details:
Salus Natural Therapy Centre
T: 01789 204775/07775558859
E: us@salusnaturaltherapy.co.uk
W: www.salusnaturaltherapy.co.uk

Practical Information:
Treatments are open to all (subject to health declaration)

Where to eat and stay:
Stratford upon Avon has numerous eateries, B&Bs and hotels within moments walk from the centre

Opening days and hours:
The centre is open Monday through Saturday throughout the year
Mon-Fri 9am-8pm, Saturday 9am-6pm

Special Offer/Incentive:
A 10% discount is available when you quote ref: DE023. Cannot be combined with any other special offer, discount or promotion.

Experiences:

Therapies Available:

- Aromatherapy Massage – relaxing and therapeutic massage with pure essential oils
- Reflexology – rebalance whole body with this gentle foot treatment
- Indian Head Massage – clear the mind and float away
- Iridology – find out what your body has in store for you, understand what the family have passed down to you from a health perspective
- Hopi Ear Candles – gently soothe away those ear and sinus pressures
- Holistic Experiences – spoil yourself with this head-to-toe experience comprising of Indian Head Massage and reflexology or choose your own combination of therapies
- Plus more ...

★ 10% DISCOUNT
When you quote REF: DE023

Ragdale Hall Health Hydro

Set in Leicestershire countryside, Ragdale Hall Health Hydro is the perfect place to enjoy a relaxing break or just a day package.

Ragdale Hall combines state-of-the-art facilities with the charm of traditional Victorian architecture to create one of the more luxurious and relaxing health resorts in the country. It is the only UK spa to have won Health Spa of the Year titles each year for the last eight (1999–2006).

Both residential stays and day visits are available.

Experiences:

Residential Stays

- *The Taster Break.* The ideal break for the first time spa visitor or for those who would like to design their own package of extra treatments. Two or three nights
- *The Ragdale Weekender.* Designed for those who want to make the most of a weekend away. It is ideal as an introduction to a new, healthier lifestyle. Two nights commencing Friday or Saturday
- *Time for Me Breaks.* Three and four night specialist breaks (six choices in total) carefully created to ensure that each precious moment of your holiday is spent pursuing your personal goals. From Pamper Me, to Relax Me to Healthier Me. There's even a 'Just for Him' too!
- *The Pampering Holiday.* The perfect five night break designed to make you feel totally refreshed and revitalised

Arrive any Sunday and leave after lunch on Friday.

Day Packages

A day at Ragdale Hall includes use of the facilities, a three course healthy buffet lunch, choice of exercise classes and use of the gym. With exception of the Late Escape arrival is 8.30–9.00am and departure 6.00pm.

- *Late Escape.* For those who want a leisurely start ... arrive at 11am, enjoy your lunch, a treatment, use of facilities and then wind down with a light supper before departure at 8:30pm
- *Refresh and Revive Day.* A day designed to do just that!
- *Chill Out.* Plenty of me time and pampering are included in this package
- *Luxury 'Pure' Days.* A choice of luxury top of the range days. Pure Bliss, Pure Nurture and Pure Detox – everyone deserves a treat

Activity Location:
Midlands

Contact Details:
Ragdale Hall
T: 01664 434 831/01664 433 000
E: enquiries@ragdalehall.co.uk
W: ragdalehall.co.uk

Practical Information:
Ragdale Hall appeals to all ages as there are such a wide range of activities and treatments on offer. Min. age 16 years
Arrival/departure for residential stays arrival is between 2pm and 4pm and departure is after lunch on your last day

Health and disability advice:
Ragdale Hall is not a medical centre and the staff are not trained medical practitioners. If you have a concern over a medical condition please consult your doctor before booking. Disabled guests should contact Ragdale before booking so that advice on suitability and practicality can be given

Gift Vouchers:
Vouchers are available in monetary amounts, for day packages or residential stays. The ideal gift at any time of year

Treatments:
Ragdale Hall has built its reputation on the quality and range of its treatments. There are a full range of traditional treatments, natural therapies and some treatments exclusively available at Ragdale Hall

new<id

new<id is the UK's largest makeover photoshoot experience company, making people of all ages look and feel amazing. You'll enjoy exemplary service with staff creating the most enjoyable, friendly, sensory, professional and personalised experience possible.

Activity Location:
Central London, Midlands, North West and Wales

Contact Details:
new<id Experiences
T: 0870 870 1299
E: info@newidstudios.co.uk
W: www.newidexperiences.com

Practical Information:
Everyone welcome! Doesn't matter who you are or how old you are – if you want to look and feel great, please visit!
Half day makeover photoshoot experiences with the UK's finest photographers presented to you in beautiful presentation boxes

Availability:
Open 7 days a week. Please call for appointment

Special Offer/Incentive:
A 10% discount is available, please quote DE06 when booking. Cannot be combined with any other special offer, discount or promotion.

★ 10% DISCOUNT
When you quote REF: DE06

Experiences:

Kids Photoshoot Experience:
The lucky child enjoys an array of magical treats to give them their ideal look. The friendly photographer will then create a wonderful portfolio of images with a range of fun backdrops and exciting props. The chosen print becomes a timeless memento.

Fashion Photoshoot Experience:
Enjoy a magical half day where dedicated experts create your perfect look: beautiful hands, stunning make-up and a glorious hair style. Step onto set to enjoy a fashion photoshoot before seeing which photograph you'll treasure forever.

Professional Hairdressing Experience:
Indulge in a professional haircut or colour (semi-permanent or 20 foils). Your experience includes an array of glorious hairdressing treatments: cleanse and condition, consultation, cut or colour, blowdry and finish.

Deluxe Fashion Experience:
Begin with a professional haircut or colour (semi-permanent or 20 foils), then enjoy a range of treatments to give you beautiful hands, stunning make-up and a glorious hair style. After your photoshoot you'll have a photograph to cherish forever.

Cedar Falls Health Spa

The magnificent 44 acres of secluded wooded landscape, calm lakes and immaculate gardens frame beautifully the handsome, red sandstone house and provide the perfect backdrop for some serious pampering. This is a health spa with a difference.

Whether you are having your nails done, losing track of time in the conservatory or enjoying some personal rejuvenation, Cedar Falls is rich with days to remember. Just a simple stroll around the grounds, surrounded by pure, fresh air will begin to lift your spirits and each morning there is a spectacular, brilliantly unrehearsed dawn chorus.

Experiences:

Sample packages include:

- *Overnight Taster.* One night's accommodation and afternoon tea. Plus two treatments from the following: aqua-jet massage, introductory facial, skin softening foot treatment, anti-ageing hand treatment
- *Naturally Holistic Two Night Delight.* Two nights' accommodation. Plus an Indian head massage or reiki and an aromatherapy mind & body massage
- *Three Night Ultimate Treat.* Three nights' accommodation. Plus an anti-ageing hand treatment, a skin-softening foot treatment, an aqua-jet massage and an introductory facial

Overnight packages include use of the facilities, exercise and relaxation classes plus all meals throughout your stay.

Pampering days include:

- *Introductory Day.* Includes a wonderful Aqua Jet Massage – this is the perfect opportunity to benefit from the Cedar Falls experience for the first time
- *Top-to-Toe Day.* This day is a favourite for many visitors to Cedar Falls and includes an Introductory Facial and a Full Body Massage

All our spa days include a three-course buffet lunch, full use of all the facilities and exercise classes.

Activity Location:
South West

Contact Details:
Cedar Falls Health Spa
T: 01823 433338
E: info@cedar-falls.co.uk
W: www.cedarfalls.co.uk

Practical Information:
Dress code is relaxed and informal during the day. Casual clothes, tracksuits and swimwear or bathrobes and slippers are all encouraged. Relaxed evening wear at dinner
Bespoke menus catering for a wide range of dietary needs (including gluten-free) can be prepared to suit any special requirement you may have

Gift Vouchers:
Vouchers give the choice of a day's pampering or overnight stays plus treatments, and can be tendered as part or total payment

Special Offer/Incentive:
A 10% discount is available. Please quote UGE01 when booking. Not to be used in conjunction with any other discount or special offer.

★ 10% DISCOUNT
When you quote REF: UGE01

Best Western Ullesthorpe Court Hotel and Golf Club

Guests are welcomed to this 17th-century property by friendly and professional staff. Located close to the motorway network, this family-owned hotel benefits from a leisure club, golf course, comfortable accommodation and conference facilities. Quality cooking is available from the Court Restaurant serving contemporary dishes and from Lincolns Brasserie, which caters for all tastes and budgets.

Activity Location:
Midlands

Contact Details:
Best Western Ullesthorpe Court Hotel and Golf Club
T: 01455 209 023
E: bookings@ullesthorpecourt.co.uk
W: www.bw-ullesthorpecourt.co.uk

Gift Vouchers:
Gift Vouchers are available in values of £5, £10 & £20 and make ideal presents for friends and family

Leisure Club:
The Leisure Club is open from 10.00am–4.00pm for Leisure Days and 7.00am–9.30pm for members with staff to assist you when required
It is advisable to book your beauty treatments well in advance

Experiences:

Getaway Breaks:
Enjoy a relaxing night away or a weekend leisure break, pamper yourself in our sauna, jacuzzi, and steam room or for the more energetic there is a fully equipped fitness room and a heated indoor swimming pool. No stay at the hotel would be complete without visiting the gold award-winning 'Utopia' beauty room. The beauty therapists offer a wide range of Decleor and Jessica treatments. Getaway Breaks are available on Bed and Breakfast rates or Dinner inclusive too.

Gold Beauty Package:
Available everyday. Includes day entry, morning coffee with biscuits, two-course healthy options lunch served in our Florida Room, afternoon tea with carrot cake and a Decleor facial incorporating a diagnostic back massage.

Golf Breaks:
All breaks are a minimum of a two-night stay and include dinner, bed & breakfast and unlimited golf; the course offers challenging greens and a number of water features, which provide an interesting round for all standards of players.

Golf Days:
Available Monday–Friday; various packages available including lunch or dinner – special winter golf days and Christmas golf day packages available too.

Grayshott Spa

Grayshott Spa is just one hour from London, set in 47 acres of gardens, adjoining 700 acres of National Trust land.

It has just completed a total renovation, re-establishing it as the leading independent spa in the UK. The Grayshott Philosophy sets out to achieve good health by using a holistic approach to natural therapy, relaxation, exercise and nutrition.

Experiences:

Treat yourself or someone special to a day of luxury and indulgence. Enjoy wonderful treatments and inspired healthy cuisine, relaxing in a beautiful tranquil environment. Our facilities include use of the spa, relaxation room, sauna, steam room, indoor and outdoor pools, gym and exercise classes. There are indoor and outdoor tennis courts where lessons can be booked with our resident pro.

- *Grayshott Spa Day.* Includes use of facilities, lunch plus a 25-minute back, neck and shoulder massage
- *Grayshott Deluxe Spa Day.* Includes use of the facilities, lunch, plus the 40-minute Grayshott Classic Massage and The Grayshott Refresher Facial
- *Total Renewal Day.* Includes use of facilities, lunch plus the Grayshott Luxury Spa Facial, aromatherapy massage, deluxe manicure or Zen Spa Pedicure and a complimentary gift to take home
- *Grayshott 2 Nights De-stress Spa Break Package.* Includes health consultation on arrival, back neck and shoulder massage, de-stress body wrap, aromatherapy back massage, all meals and use of facilities
- *Grayshott 3 Nights Sport Fitness Break.* Includes health consultation on arrival, dietary consultation, fitness assessment, personal training, 50-minute reviving massage, all meals and use of facilities

Activity Location:
Surrey

Contact Details:
Grayshott Spa
T: 01428 602020
E: reservations@grayshottspa.com
W: www.grayshottspa.com

Practical Information:
18 years or over, or 16 years if accompanied by an adult

Availability:
Open 365 days per year. Minimum two night stay or Spa Days

Gift Vouchers:
Available for all occasions

Booking Info:
Maximum group booking of six persons

Special Offer/Incentive
A 10% discount is available to readers on all Spa Days and Spa Breaks but not on individual treatments. Not combinable with any other offer and excludes Christmas and New Year. Quote Direct Experiences when booking.

★ **10% DISCOUNT** (see text)
Please mention Direct Experiences when booking

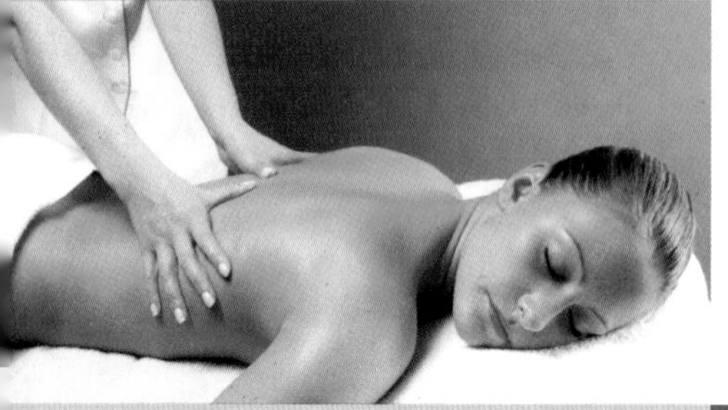

Best Western Sketchley Grange Hotel and Spa

Our stylish four star hotel and spa is ideal for you to get away from the hustle and bustle of everyday life. Relax and be pampered on our 'Girlies at the Grange Package' – everything you need to help you unwind.

Activity Location:
Midlands

Contact Details:
Niki or Catherine
Best Western Sketchley Grange Hotel & Spa
T: 01455 251133
E: reservations@sketchleygrange.co.uk
W: www.bw-sketchleygrange.co.uk

Special Offer/Incentive:
A 10% discount is available when you quote ref DE07 when booking. Cannot be combined with any other special offers, discounts or promotions.

★ 10% DISCOUNT
When you quote REF: DE07

Experiences:

Girlies at the Grange Package includes the following.

- Three beauty treatments consisting of:
  - 30-minute Jessica Manicure
  - Essential Oil Facial
  - Back Massage
- Three-course dinner from our Girlies at the Grange special menu in the Terrace Bistro
- Overnight accommodation followed by a full English breakfast
- Full use of Romans Health & Leisure facilities including 17-metre award winning swimming pool, spa, steam room, sauna and fully equipped gymnasium

You can also add any of the following to your package at an additional cost:

- Champagne and strawberries
- Healthy Options two course lunch taken in the Terrace Bistro
- Three-course dinner in the Willow Restaurant (subject to availability)
- Upgrade your bedroom to a Junior or Master Suite
- Additional beauty packages are available (subject to availability)

re-aqua salons & spas

re-aqua is the leading collection of well-being and beauty therapy salons and spas in the UK. Our pampering experiences provide a perfect gift for every occasion. No matter which package you choose to be pampered with, be assured you will notice a difference. We'll make sure the biggest difference is how you feel – both inside and out!

Experiences:

- *Two of a Kind Pamper.* Pampering experience for two people. Treat you and your friend, partner or mother – to a truly relaxing visit with both of you taking your appointments on the same day
- *Bliss Pamper.* Give someone special a bit of TLC to some quality pampering
- *Top-to-Toe Pamper.* Indulge in four pampering treatments ... Just the thing that will make you feel completely pampered and totally stress-free
- *Spa Taster Half Day at re-aqua Holmes Place.** Slip into a luxury robe and don a pair of slippers and enjoy some serious relaxation, taking advantage of the spa's facilities with a choice of a treatment
- *VIP Pamper Package for Men.* Give the man in your life some real loving
- *Deluxe Day at the Gatsby Spa.** A relaxing experience of pure indulgence at the Gatsby Spa Bromley
- *City Half Hour of Heaven.** Pop out of the office for 30 minutes and go back to your desk in a new body
- *City Handy Half Hour.** Slip away from your desk for only 30 minutes for the handiest half-hour ever

Activity Location:
Nationwide
re-aqua pamper packages are available at any of the 29 re-aqua outlets nationwide except those which are salon specific and indicated*. Salon opening times may vary, but are generally open from Monday to Saturday, 9.00am–6.00pm. Certain salon terms and conditions may apply. Please check with the salon prior to booking.

Contact Details:
re-aqua salons & spas
T: 0870 403 0002
E: info@re-aqua.co.uk
W: www.re-aqua.co.uk

Where to buy:
To purchase your voucher please visit our website www.re-aqua.co.uk or call telesales on 0870 403 002 during normal office hours

What happens next:
You will receive an information pack and an open-dated voucher valid for 12 months. Booking a date couldn't be easier. After receiving your pack, simply telephone the number detailed in your information pack and we will do the rest. It is advised that you book a date at least four weeks in advance. However, last minute places are sometimes available

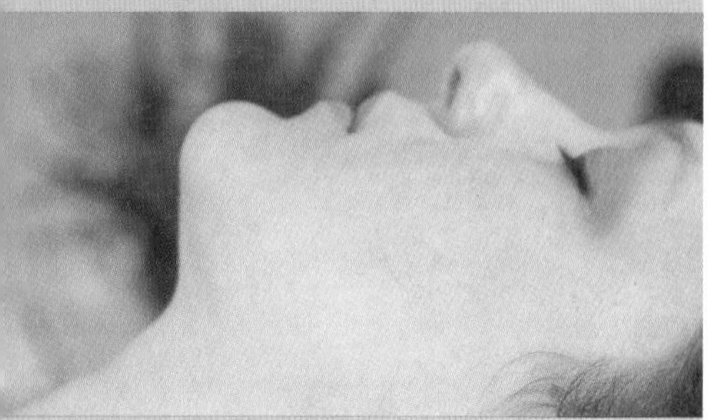

Earth Mother

Earth Mother is a holistic haven located in the picturesque town of Ramsbottom in Lancashire. Launched by holistic therapists and natural beauty experts Rachel and Joanna Kelly, Earth Mother is founded on the sisters' lifelong passion for a natural, ethical approach to health and beauty. Visit Earth Mother and experience heavenly holistic therapy treatments, guaranteed to restore health and happiness, calm the senses and soothe the soul.

Location:
North West

Contact Details:
Earth Mother
T: 01706 828333
E: info@earthmotherstore.co.uk
W: www.earthmotherstore.co.uk

Bespoke Packages:
Earth Mother can create bespoke packages to match individual holistic needs (please enquire for more details)

Gift Vouchers:
Gift vouchers are available for all packages

Special Offer/Incentive:
Free Earth Mother Soul Sister Mandarin Lip Balm per treatment (quote *Ultimate Gift Experiences* on booking).

Experiences:

- *Reflexology.* This ancient Chinese and Indian diagnostic and therapeutic system massages reflex zones of the feet to restore the body's balance and health
- *Shiatsu.* This Japanese healing therapy aims to enhance self-healing of both body and mind by rebalancing our energy
- *Reiki.* This ancient healing system is based on channelling universal energy and is deeply relaxing
- *Body Massage.* This relaxing treatment will help to heal discomfort and improve your sense of well-being. A massage can be given to the whole body, or can focus on specific areas
- *Prescriptive Facial.* This unique bespoke facial will be personalised to your skin type, to purify, replenish and soothe your skin, restoring natural glow
- *Aqua Detox.* Detoxify and re-balance the body with this unique treatment usually given through the feet
- *Indian Head Massage.* This ancient Ayurvedic healing system uses a variety of massage techniques on the shoulders, upper arms and neck as well as head, and can be tailored to suit all individual needs
- *Food Sensitivity Testing.* This non-invasive test measures your sensitivity to over 150 food and drink items and will help you to avoid foods that compromise your health and well-being

Water

'Nice? It's the ONLY thing' said the Water Rat solemnly, as he leant forward for his stroke. 'Believe me, my young friend, there is NOTHING – absolutely nothing – half so much worth doing as simply messing about in boats.'

KENNETH GRAHAME, THE WIND IN THE WILLOWS

Messing about in boats

Wherever there is a puddle deep enough to float a boat in you can be sure to find someone trying to sail, powerboat or windsurf.

Water sports cover the full spectrum from serene sailing to flying spray and adrenaline rush. On a calm sunny day it is as tranquil and elegant a sport as you could wish for, if lying back and watching the cat's paws of wind toying with a sail can honestly be called a sport. At the other extreme a Zap Cat inflatable racing catamaran, bouncing off the wave tops as the outboard roars disapproval, can be every bit as white knuckle as white-water sports.

Getting afloat

Most introductory sailing courses start with a brief introduction to the parts of the boat, the rigging, and a few basic nautical terms before launching into the control of sail and steering by means of the tiller and the sheets (the ropes that control sails). After that you're off, learning to turn with the wind behind you (gybe) or to zigzag across the face of it (tack) so that you can complete a triangular course.

We don't (yet) have compulsory licences for sailing so it's up to you how much or little tuition you want to take, though I would strongly recommend the Royal Yachting Association (RYA) dinghy sailing course in the UK and its equivalents worldwide for the mix of a little theory and a lot of practical application. A couple of weekends – or three or four days on the beach – is all you need to come away with a little certification and a big dollop of confidence.

Sailing takes no time to learn and years to master, so you can be up and running in an hour or so and sailing happily for the rest of your life. You may be content to simply noodle around in circles, reliving childrens stories from your youth, or you may want to speed things up a bit by starting to race. Racing is commonly seen as the best way of learning in a hurry. It takes a bit of commonsense so as not to get in the way of others, but most clubs are more than happy to encourage beginners to have a go. There is no quicker way of gaining boat-handling skills and recognising those fine touches that distinguish the master mariners from those merely messing about (perfectly noble ambition though that is).

The need for speed – Zap Cats

For some the idea of power at sea is an abomination against nature. I challenge even those purists not to enjoy Zap Catting. Zap Cats have been described as the 'Lotus Elise of the sea' and they are the perfect solution to those who have speed demon tendencies but are too young or simply too dangerous to be allowed out on roads. The normal starting point is a couple of hours introductory session with two participants and an instructor. If you're wondering why you've been given a crash helmet then you won't be wondering for long as these wildly overpowered lightweights leap over the waves. Bring a camera, and make sure it's waterproof.

Windsurfing

Once windsurfing boards were big, heavy and mean. I remember spending pretty much an entire day falling off into the water and clumsily climbing back out again. Just to break up the routine a little I would occasionally indulge in brief, clammy, full-contact bouts with the sail before going in off the other side.

These days modern composite materials, plus the use of bracing in the sail itself, has resulted in light, taut, much easier-to-handle rigs; and with it a much more enjoyable learning curve for the beginner and a world of possibilities for the master. It still takes a while before you'll be able to stand upright (imagine wrestling a wet sheet while balancing on an ironing board) but once you've got the basics you will feel uniquely part of the wind and waves as you slice and carve your way across the surface of the ocean.

Inner space

For the real purists boats are passé. The real deal is to disappear from sight altogether and let the water swallow you up as you weightlessly explore the 'inner space' that covers seven-tenths of the planet.

Scuba diving is the closest most of us will ever get to being astronauts. You are immersed in an alien environment, weightless and slow moving while creatures straight from the pages of sci-fi novels pootle about unconcernedly.

Diving qualifications get as complex as you can wish, but the major organisations all offer a very basic entry point to get you diving right here, right now to see if you like it – even for kids as young as ten. After that the world's your oyster – and remember a full seven-tenths of it is underwater.

Bateaux London

Bateaux London operates the luxury River Thames restaurant cruise brand of Catamaran Cruisers. Combining fresh menus, live entertainment, 5-star customer care and breathtaking views of London, Bateaux London caters for both the leisure and business markets, with daily departures from Embankment Pier.

Experiences:

Packages:
Lunch and dinner cruises operate 7 days per week. Boats can accommodate parties from 45 to 220 people for business use or for smaller groups. There are also 'special touch' packages available for 2-24 people.

Private Charters:
Bateaux London is experienced in hosting events, from cocktail receptions, birthday and wedding celebrations, corporate entertainment, product launches, meetings and seminars. Menus can be designed to suit each function, so each event/booking is tailored to exact customer requirements.

Catamaran Cruisers:
Offers the best sightseeing cruises on the River Thames. With a fleet of six vessels, Catamaran Cruises have Circular Cruises, offering a professional multilingual commentary in nine different languages via headsets. This 50-minute non-stop Thames River Cruise departs hourly from Westminster Pier.

Point-to-point cruises offer London visitors the flexibility to explore riverside attractions on a single or return basis. Departing regularly from Embankment, Waterloo (London Eye), Bankside, Tower and Greenwich Piers.

Activity Location:
Greater London

Contact details:
Bateaux London
T: 0207 9252215
E: info@bateauxlondon.com
W: www.bateauxlondon.com

Availability:
7 days per week

Gift Vouchers:
Gift vouchers are available for:

- Three-course set lunch
- Sunday lunch jazz cruise, three-course set menu
- Dinner cruise, with on-board entertainment and a four-course à la carte menu

Special Offer/Incentive
10% discount Bateaux London lunch and dinner cruises (excludes special events).
20% discount on catamaran cruises, point-to-point and circular cruises (excludes tickets with 3rd parties).

★ **10-20% DISCOUNT** (see text)
Please mention Direct Experiences when booking

DiverCity

DiverCity is a one stop dive centre. You can go from complete beginner to a fully fledged professional diver with us. For the complete beginner we offer 'Try Dives' where you take your first underwater breaths under the direct supervision of one of our instructors. The next step is the Professional Association of Diving Professionals (PADI) Open Water Diver (OWD) course.

Activity Location:
Milton Keynes

Contact details:
Divercity
T: 01908 647300/0870 7518288
E: info@divercityscuba.com
W: www.divercityscuba.com

Practical Information:
For Try Dives, swimming costumes/shorts, towel and T-shirt are required
All other diving equipment is supplied
Age restrictions – 12 years +
Brief medical questionnaire must be completed before diving

Gift Vouchers:
Gift vouchers are available for Try Dives, parties, schools, corporate events and nights out

Additional Information:
DiverCity has an online shop
Divercity Diving Club membership gives discounted rates on a range of diving activities

Experiences:

Try Diving:
DiverCity arranges Try Dives at local community swimming pools in Beds, Bucks and Herts, during evening and weekends.

Training:
DiverCity has built a reputation resulting in receiving the 'Instructor Development Centre' status – the award given by PADI to centres it entrusts to train its instructors and dive leaders. Safety, service and professionalism are key components in the merits of this status.

Some of the courses available include:

PDI Open Water Diver, PDI Advanced Diver, PDI/EFR Rescue Diver, PDI Master Scuba Diver, PDI Diving Specialities, PDI pro courses, TDI Technical Diving courses.

DiverCity can also arrange diving holidays in the UK, 'Mega Dives' in the North Pole and White Sea ice diving and in the sun holidays 'Luxury Egyptian Live aboard'

Glide3

Glide3 is a young, vibrant company providing unique and exciting hovercraft experiences near Basildon, Essex. We look forward to entertaining you in your priceless time off. Experiences are available as gift vouchers, individual bookings or as group activities. If you want something a little extra, we can create your own perfect event.

Experiences:

Glide3 Hovercraft Experience:

One of the reasons that this experience is so unique is that you get to fly the hovercraft on *land* and *water* (not all hovercraft experiences have water included on the course). I have developed a *challenging course for you* that is almost a 50:50 split between land and water – the way I look at it is, you may as well be on wheels if you're haven't got water! You will marvel at the hovercraft's unique ability to glide from *land to water* and back again – that's what makes it special, so it's important that *you get the full experience*!

- Experience the full potential of a hovercraft, when you fly across land and water
- Pure adrenaline rush as you execute 360° and 180° spins on water
- Exclusive access to this unique hovercraft
- Enjoy exclusive attention and become a pro with our one-on-one tuition and learn quickly and safely with confidence
- Luxuriate in the privacy of a private lake and escape to your own world
- Be safe and sound in highest quality, safety and communications equipment

Activity Location:
South East

Contact Details:
Glide3 Limited
T: 0845 226 0748
E: info@glide3.com
W: www.glide3.com

Practical Information:
You and your guests will be watered and fed with *free* snacks and refreshments throughout
Remember your experience forever with a professionally taken photograph
Friends and family are welcome to come and watch you

Availability:
You can book this experience for any day of the week. Call 0845 226 0748 to book

Special Offer/Incentive:
For extra special attention and the best offers, call and mention you saw us in the Direct Experiences book.

Mountain Water Experience

Mountain Water Experience is one of the premier residential adventurous activity and field study centres in Devon and the South West. With a host of natural activity and study sites close by we are certain you will have an experience to remember.

We are proud of our ability to offer a bespoke service, with a wide range of tailor-made outdoor adventurous activity options for both children and adults. All of our instructors are highly qualified and experienced. Our commitment to safety is second to none.

Activity Location:
South West

Contact Details:
Mountain Water Experience
T: 01548 550 675
E: mwe@mountainwaterexperience.com
W: www.mountainwaterexperience.com

Practical Information:
All activities are subject to weather conditions
Courses include instruction, use of specialist equipment and transport between our centre and the activity site. Lunch is not included
Min. age 10 years
Min. number of participants for activity to run: six people

Availability:
The MWE centre is open all year. Bookings taken no more than two weeks in advance

Experiences:

We've got the answer for those of you looking for that bit extra – something a little different.

Let us take you, your family or friends out for the day or half day to do some of those activities you wished you'd always had a go at or have wanted to try again. Maybe in a different environment, a little higher, deeper or wetter.

We have a wide range of adventurous activity options both at our centre site and further afield using the Dartmoor National Park or the South Devon coast:

- Kayaking
- Climbing
- Body Boarding
- Caving
- Assault Course
- Crate Stacking
- Moorland Guided Walks
- Climbing Wall
- Surfing
- Canoe River Trips
- Coasteering
- Gorge Walking
- Coastal Guided Walks
- Abseiling

Saber Powersports Ltd

Looking for an experience you will never forget?

Saber Powersports have been providing powerboat experiences for over 17 years. Travelling at high speed across the water is unique – an exhilarating experience like no other.

Experiences:

Your experience begins with a safety briefing and an introduction to the boat. You then get changed into the Saber Powersports racing team kit and safety gear. Then it's onto the water. Our boats have comfortable secure seating and the experience is suitable for all adventure seekers.

RIB Powerboat Experience (1½ hours):
Feel the power of our 8m 225h.p. Offshore Racing Rib doing a high speed banked corner. Experience the thrill of wave jumping – in the hands of our experienced instructors these boats will fly above the water.

Drive a Honda Race Boat (2 hours):
The Honda Formula 4-Stroke championship (HF4S) is the largest, most exciting offshore powerboat series in the world. Feel the speed and grace of this highly responsive racing machine.

Drive the HTM SR24 (2½ Hours):
The HTM is one of the fastest production powerboats in the world. She can power through almost any water at high speed sending the boat flying high above the surface. This high-performance wild cat demands respect – would you like to put her through her paces?

Activity Location:
South East

Contact Details:
Saber Powersports Ltd
T: 02380 016253
E: info@sabermarine.com
W: www.sabermarine.com

Practical Information:
Highly charged waterborne white-knuckle ride
You must be over 16 years old, and weigh no more than 120 kg
Not suitable for those with a serious back or heart complaint or for pregnant women. If in doubt ask!
The experience times include a safety briefing, driving time and a debriefing. You must arrive 20 minutes prior to your start time
Spectators are welcome to wave you off from the shore. Full catering and car parking on site
Please dress warmly, with non-slip shoes (e.g. trainers or deck shoes). Waterproofs and safety equipment will be provided
Bear in mind that there is a high wind-chill factor aboard the boat! Bring a change of clothes just in case

Availability:
We run selected days from April–Sept (see www.sabermarine.com for booking dates)

Special Offer/Incentive:
Save up to £45 on these unique experiences:

RIB Powerboat Experience (1½ hours)
Normally £60 – special offer £50

Drive a Honda Race Boat (two hours)
Normally £110 – special offer £90

Drive the HTM SR24 (two and a half hours)
Normally £150 – special offer £125

Ultimate Powerboat Day: drive the Honda *and* HTM
Normally £240 – special offer £195

★ SAVE UP TO £45
See details above

Team Powerboating

Team Powerboating has been trading for 18 years and is the RYA's only approved race boat training school in the UK offering either taster days – before taking up the sport – or individual race days for that special occasion.

Also corporate events tailor-made for companies looking for something completely different to offer their clients or staff.

Location:
Midlands

Contact details:
Team Powerboating
T: 0870 752 4799
E: teampowerboating@ntlworld.com
W: www.teampowerboating.co.uk

Practical information:
Max weight 18 stone. Min. height 5 ft 2 in. Max. height 6 ft 2 in
Maximum girth around chest and upper arms 56 in

Health Restrictions:
Those who suffer from epilepsy or a medical condition which prohibits driving will not be accepted. We have a policy of nil tolerance to alcohol and drugs

Equipment:
All safety equipment is provided

Validity:
Selected days from April to October inclusive

Gift Vouchers:
Available on request

Special Offer/Incentive:
20% discount on individual race days. Special offers on corporate bookings on request.

★ **20% DISCOUNT**
On individual race days

Experiences:

Individual Race Days:
A full day driving single-seater racing boats, hydroplanes, catamarans and monohulls.

Full one-to-one training – exciting circuit – expect 30 plus laps. Buffet lunch and tea included – guests welcome – free T-shirt and commemorative certificate.

Corporate Days – Speedway Challenge:
A corporate day with a difference – exciting Hydroplane Speedway Challenge tailor-made to the clients specification – ideal for staff reward or customer day out.

Full catering to suit day. Champagne presentation plus commemorative gift and certificate.

Treasure Trails:
Includes Speedway trials, Powerboat Obstacle Course, Zapcats, Ringo Rides and RHIB Rides and other water based challenges. Treasure trail with clues to find and questions to answer.

Full catering to suit the day. *You will get wet!* Commemorative gift and certificate.

Vortex Racing Ltd/Vortex Events

Vortex Events create and deliver professional corporate events, effective teambuilding with fun-filled activities for your staff and customers – challenges, product launches, hospitality, sales incentives and charters, whatever the occasion or size of event.

Our speciality is Zapcats, not only do we race these in the National Championships but we also deliver some amazing experiences, stag and hen days and corporate events.

Activity Location:
Southampton, London and other locations by arrangement

Contact details:
Vortex Racing Ltd
T: 0870 7775598
E: info@vortex-events.com
W: www.vortex-events.com

Practical Information:
Dry suits and all necessary safety equipment provided

Gift Vouchers:
A range of gift vouchers can be purchased from us or via the Vortex on-line shop

Additional Information:
Zapcat Experiences are available nearly all year round on weekend dates from Southampton and other UK locations

Special Offers:
A 10% discount is available for readers. Please mention Direct Experiences when booking. Cannot be combined with any other promotion, offer or discount.

Experiences:

Experience is everything ... just imagine for a moment ... you hold on tight as the awesome power of an amazing catamaran accelerates you across the water ... you hold on even tighter and laugh or scream as this unbelievable machine throws you into a 3-g turn ... you're spinning on a sixpence and then, as the speed increases you feel the breathtaking pull ... you hit the surf and you're airborne!!!

This is the thrill of a zapcat!

With a power-to-weight ratio of 340bhp per tonne (that's greater than a Ferrari Testarossa) and cornering that can only be compared to a Formula One car, these immense boats really do have it all.

The adventure is an adrenaline pumping, pure power, action-packed ride where five minutes seems like an hour.

Safety is paramount and our highly skilled staff will look after everything. Safety equipment is provided including top-of-the-range dry suits so you won't even get wet!

Vortex guarantees an exhilarating day out on our RIBs and Zapcat powerboats.

- Corporate events
- Activity experiences
- Stag and hen parties
- Boat charter
- Zapcat sales

★ **10% DISCOUNT** Please mention Direct Experiences when booking

WakeMK

Waterskiing and wakeboarding has been around for ages, but over the last three years wakeboarding has become the fastest growing water sport activity in the country. With the advancement of cable ski facilities the cost of participating has been greatly reduced and this has opened up the doors to people of all ages and abilities. This high-speed, adrenaline-filled sport is guaranteed to put a smile on your face.

WakeMK is one of the best places to learn – our team of friendly professional instructors are dedicated to helping you improve.

Activity Location:
South East

Contact Details:
Wake MK
T: 01908 670197
E: info@wakemk.com
W: www.wakemk.com

Practical Information:
Min. age 8 years
Weight less than 19 stone
Must be able to swim 50 m

Recommended:
Bring swim shorts and a towel

Availability:
Between 2–7 days per week depending on the season

Gift Vouchers:
Available from £25–£600

Corporate/Groups:
WakeMK is an ideal venue for group bookings. We can cater for all sizes of groups and offer discounted sessions

Special Offer:
10% discount available to readers. Please mention Direct Experiences when booking. Cannot be combined with any other discounts or promotional offers.

★ **10% DISCOUNT** Please mention Direct Experiences when booking

Experiences:

The two-hour progression course starts with a full safety briefing and swiftly moves along to getting you on the water and round the cable. Kneeboarding is the first step on the ladder, a simple discipline which helps you understand the basics. Once you have mastered the corners we will get you up and around on a wakeboard or pair of water-skis by the end of the two hours.

No doubt you will be booking your next session straight away, with our high success rate and the addictive rush you gain from skimming across the surface of the water; we know we will see you again soon!

Whitecap Leisure - Willen Lake

Based in Milton Keynes, Whitecap Leisure provides a range of water sports. Whether you want to take part in one of the certified courses or an activity package - Whitecap aim to maximise your water sports experience to suit the individual or group. The team comprises of fully qualified and experienced instructors, coaches and trainers, with safety being the priority.

Activity Location:
Milton Keynes

Contact details:
Whitecap Leisure
T: 01908 691630
E: admin@whitecap.co.uk
W: www.whitecap.co.uk

Additional Information:
All specialist equipment for activities is provided by Whitecap Leisure
All participants must be able to swim 25m unaided and must be confident in the water
Adequate levels of fitness are required

Special Offer:
A 10% discount is available to readers. Please mention Direct Experiences when booking. Cannot be combined with any other discounts or promotional offers.

Experiences:

- *Full Day's Powerboating Experience.* Full day (9.30am–4.30pm) on the water, spend the morning learning to drive a 140hp inshore rib powerboat and then move on to the high-speed manoeuvres in the afternoon. The perfect present for anyone who is up for a bit of speed and excitement. Group size is never more than four people ensuring great value for money
- *Introduction to Kayak Racing.* Learn to paddle a stable racing kayak. The course concentrates on forward paddling techniques using the progressive fleet of kayaks
- *Windsurfing Taster Session.* Three hours during which you will learn all the basics to get sailing. You will start on our land-based simulator before going afloat. By the end of the lesson you will be able to sail and steer your board across the wind
- *Royal Yachting Association Level 1.* This introductory course is designed for those with little or no sailing experience. It is held over two days, from 9.15am–1.30pm each day. Our qualified instructors will guide you through the basics of learning to sail; through a combination of on-land and on-water teaching you will achieve a standard where you are competent and confident enough to sail around a triangular course. Either in single-handed (S/H) or double-handed (D/H) dinghies
- *Introduction to Paddlesports.* The sheltered waters of Willen Lake are a great place to learn to control a kayak or canoe. Our experienced coaches will introduce you to the thrill and freedom of being afloat – looking after your safety while you learn the basic strokes. One day provides an introduction to the sport. All specialist equipment provided

★ **10% DISCOUNT** Please mention Direct Experiences when booking

Current Trends

Current Trends are a rafting and coaching centre on the banks of the river Trent in Nottingham. We use the facilities at the National Water Sports Centre.

Current Trends were one of the first companies to bring rafting into the UK and have been growing ever since.

We are one of the few centres with an online booking facility and pride ourselves on our wide range of knowledge and connections in the paddling world.

Activity Location:
Midlands

Contact Details:
Current Trends
T: 0115 981 88 44
E: info@currenttrends.co.uk
W: www.currenttrends.co.uk

Practical Information:
Max. weight 15 stone
Min. age 18 years
All rafters must be water confident and able to swim 50m
We advise mothers-to-be and people with troubled backs not to raft
Spectators may view from the path running down the side of the river at no extra charge

Equipment:
Safety equipment is provided and full wet suits can be hired. Please note that our wet suits do not include footwear so please bring a pair of trainers with you that you are happy to get wet. If you do not wish to hire a wet suit you may bring your own or wear a tracksuit top and bottoms

Weather Restrictions:
Flood, high winds, electric storms, drought could result in the activity being cancelled

Special Offer:
A 10% discount is available to readers. Please mention Direct Experiences when booking. Cannot be combined with any other discounts or promotional offers.

★ **10% DISCOUNT** Please mention Direct Experiences when booking

Experiences:

Rafting Individuals:
Experience the thrill of the rapids on our grade 2/3 white water course in Nottingham. A qualified guide will aid you in your descent of the rapids.

- Availability: On selected weekends and weekdays between March and December
- Course duration: 2 hours
- Course numbers: There will be a maximum of 8 people in your raft plus your guide

Private Rafts for 6–8 People:
Book an exclusive raft for your group. Great for parties and corporate groups.

- Availability: Weekends when booking more than two rafts
- Course duration: 2 hours
- Course numbers: 10–32 people

Rapid Running for 2 People:
Experience the excitement of steering your own mini raft down the course. A great follow on from rafting.

- Availability: Selected weekends and weekdays between March and October
- Course duration: 2 hours
- Course numbers: 2 people

Rescue Consultancy Services - Powerboat Training School

The powerboat training scheme has been designed and aimed at sport boat owners and operators, whether connected with sailing, sub-aqua diving, water sports or rescue activities.

The Royal Yachting Association (RYA) courses have been developed to provide you with a sound practical knowledge of the techniques of boat handling on coastal and inland waters.

This will result in a nationally recognised Level 1 and Level 2 certification.

Experiences:

Holding instructional courses at our Plymouth location, with a detailed syllabus that includes care and maintenance of the boat, recovery, handling under way, anchoring, pre-launch planning, slow manoeuvring and high-speed rough water control.

Typical course profile in outline:

Day 1
Evening registration at centre.

Day 2
Introduction, classroom theory, slipway launching (with practical on water instruction) and slipway boat retrieval.

Day 3
Passage planning in lecture room, slipway launching, rough water handling at speed (weather permitting), lunch and boat retrieval.

Activity Location:
South West

Contact Details:
Rescue Consultancy Services
T: 01455 213002/0777 569 7936
E: john@rcs-powerboat-training.co.uk
W: www.rcs-powerboat-training.co.uk

School Boats:
Picton Nautique 7.5m 200 Mercury
Picton 6.2m 135 Mercury
Humber 5.8m 150 Yamaha

Practical Information:
Courses held in Plymouth
Accommodation is provided in single and multiple occupancy rooms
All prices include bed/breakfast for two nights, boats and lifejackets, RYA Level 2 certificate fee, boat fuel, lecture pack and packed lunches
All instructors are RYA trained and approved
Corporate and group specialist days available upon request

Special Offer/Incentive:
A 10% discount is available to readers – please mention Direct Experiences when booking. Cannot be combined with any other offers or promotions.

★ **10% DISCOUNT** Please mention Direct Experiences when booking

Ondeck Sailing

Ondeck Sailing offers a diverse range of sailing activities to suit everyone. Based in the Solent, we specialise in RYA qualifications, yacht charters, yacht racing, Caribbean regattas, adventure destinations, corporate hospitality and team-building packages.

The flotilla of yachts provide something for everyone from high-performance racing to comfortable cruising, competitive enough to be available to yachtsmen and women of all abilities.

Activity Location:
South East

Contact details:
Ondeck Sailing
T: 0845 1662024
E: enquiry@ondeck.co.uk
W: www.ondeck.co.uk

Practical Information:
Life jackets and safety harnesses provided
All yachts are equipped to required standards

Experiences:

Sailing Sea School:
Can be enjoyed by people of all ages and abilities. Ondeck teach safe sailing techniques whilst fostering a respect and love for the sea. From its base in Gosport, Ondeck offers a complete RYA practical and theory sail training programme both on the water and in the classroom.

Individual Group Sailing:
A range of sailing activities for individual berths and groups at all levels. Racing, instructional cruising, transatlantic passages or weekend mile building trips are just some of the activities offered. On fleets of 40-ft and 65-ft performance yachts, each yacht being run by experienced professional skippers and mates.

Yachts can also be chartered for the day, weekend or specific events, a professional skipper and mate (for Farr 65s) is included as is wet weather gear and life jackets.

Corporate:
Ondeck can provide corporate sailing activities from corporate hospitality events and team building days to premium racing events and industry regattas.

Hovercraft for Hire

Riding on a cushion of air, the hovercraft provides a truly unique experience. With simple throttle and steering controls it needn't take long to learn the principles of driving a hovercraft, but the exhilaration will keep you endlessly enthralled.

Experiences:

Hovercraft Experience:

The land and water hovercraft experience combines the best of everything. There's the thrill of flying at speed from water to land and back again; the challenge of mastering a new skill; and of course the fun of not always getting it right.

Our single-seater hovercraft are safe and easy to drive, but still provide an unusual test of co-ordination skills, which makes it almost as much fun to watch as it is to do. This is truly a unique and exhilarating activity which can be enjoyed by almost anyone.

These events last up to three hours and driving is shared between up to five participants.

Family Fun:

The land and water hovercraft experience is also suitable for the whole family. It is great fun and there is something for everyone – drives for the adults and rides for the youngsters.

Group Activities:

The ultimate challenge for groups of up to 12 people. After a short briefing from your instructor you will take the controls and fly solo. As you become more confident you will progress to more challenging manoeuvres until as last you experience the thrill of flying at speed from land to water. And while you take a breather from the action you can watch and learn as your friends tackle the circuit.

Activity Location:
Midlands

Contact Details:
Hovercraft for Hire
T: 01949 831577/07711 098798
E: Jeremy@hovercraft-hire.co.uk
W: www.hovercraft-hire.co.uk

Practical Information:
Min. age to drive 17 years although youngsters may take part as passengers
All safety equipment and waterproofs are provided

Availability:
Pre-booking is essential

Special Offer/Incentive:
A 10% discount is available – please mention *Ultimate Gift Experiences* when booking. Cannot be combined with any other discounts or promotional offers.

★ **10% DISCOUNT** Please mention *Ultimate Gift Experiences* when booking

Unusual and quirky

'Nothing is a waste of time if you use the experience wisely.'

AUGUSTE RODIN, SCULPTOR

Oddball outings

What do you get for the person who's got everything?

Easy, read on.

There are things to do out there that can make trainspotters of any of us. For your dyed-in-the-wool hardcore train fan there is the possibility of learning to drive a steam train. Would-be Casey Joneses can take the controls and buffer up the engine to the brake van. If you're very good you can even blow the whistle. Meantime the rest of the family can take a ride on any number of nostalgic steam trains, often with a hint of luxury for those not entirely convinced by the hardware alone.

Bang on target

If machinery doesn't motivate the person you're looking to buy a present for then try a change of target. Clay pigeon shooting is a means of hefting a twelve bore to your shoulder and letting fly with both barrels, only without the blood and fluttering feathers. A clay pigeon shooting lesson will get you outdoors, under the supervision of a qualified shooter who will show you how to load, reload and fire before you ready yourself for hordes of incoming clay disks. Sort of like Space Invaders only with a lot more smoke and noise.

Of course if the noise is a problem (and it shouldn't be – you'll have ear protectors on) you can always learn the true meaning of silent but deadly with the aid of bow and arrow. I always thought there were only two types of bow – crossbow and longbow, but it turns out that there are at least four. While longbows still exist for the historically minded, they are quite demanding and not that accurate, so you're more likely to find yourself facing the friendly end of a recurve (aka Olympic or take down bow) or a compound bow. Compound bows are the high-tech end of things and suited to the kind of person who knows what Kevlar and carbon composites are, and probably owns things made of them already. Recurve bows are based on a Mongolian design and can be made of various materials, but the beginners' end of the market is largely wooden and so that's what you're going to find in your sticky little hands.

Bows come in different 'draw' strengths which means that anyone, including the kids, can be kitted out with a bow to let them shoot hell out of the targets.

Just remember that it's illegal to go hunting anything at all with a bow. If you want to do that then what you're after is paintball which means your nearest, dearest and the boss all come under the category of 'target'.

Stars in their eyes

If you want to give a gift that lasts a lifetime then one idea is to name a star after your special somebody. Your chosen person will be immortalised by having a star of your choice named after them and will receive a package containing a certificate detailing telescopic co-ordinates of the star so that they can pick out exactly which one bears their moniker.

If naming a star isn't enough, why not make somebody a star by treating them to a professional recording or photography session. A team of professional sound engineers or portrait photographers will work with you to create an experience that will not only be great at the time but will also last as a recording or photograph for you to keep. So if somebody you know thinks they're the next Arctic Monkeys or Kate Moss, why not give them a chance to shine?

Tree hugging

Along the same lines as naming a star for somebody is the possibility of purchasing a tree on behalf of your gift recipient. Somewhat more down to earth than star naming, this gift also helps contribute to reforestation and will be a welcome gift for the 'green' person in your life. They'll take pleasure from knowing that you've really thought about a gift that gives twice – to both them and the planet.

For the romantic among us there is also the opportunity to experience an eco-break. Set in beautiful countryside settings, these are perfect opportunities to experience a more relaxed, nature-friendly holiday where you escape from the pressures of modern life and have the chance to really get back in touch with the environment – and each other. With the chance to experience some natural relaxation therapies too this could be the most laid-back break you've ever taken.

There is such a wide variety of experiences available that, no matter how unusual your gift needs, you should be able to find something to suit your requirements.

Eco Retreats - Romantic Tipi Retreat for Couples

Relax on a romantic Eco-break in your own individually designed Native American Tipi.

Discover comfort and luxury in harmony with a beautiful natural environment - in the heart of the Welsh mountains.

On an Eco retreat you can reconnect with the rhythms of the environment, experience the benefits of holistic therapy and gain understanding of Eco-related issues through a visit to the world's foremost Eco centre.

Experiences:

Get away from it all in a stunningly beautiful, secluded location, surrounded by breathtaking walks through hills and ancient woods.

During your stay in a lovingly furnished tipi you'll be offered a Reiki healing treatment, meditation session and voucher to visit the Centre for Alternative Technology.

You'll find the space to reconnect to each other free from the distractions of modern life, space to unwind and recharge your batteries.

Your 21-ft Tipi is built from sustainable products in the style of the original structures inhabited by Native American Indians for centuries. The tipis are surprisingly spacious and provide a comfortable home all year round. By day they are bright and fresh and by night you'll find nothing can beat snuggling up by a cosy fire.

Activity Location:
Wales

Contact Details:
Eco Retreats
T: 01654 781375/07702 598909
E: chanan@ecoretreats.co.uk
W: www.ecoretreats.co.uk

Practical Information:
Minimum age - 18 years

Equipment:
All you need to bring is food and appropriate clothing

Availability:
Open from mid/late April through to late October. Retreats usually for two nights but contact us to discuss alternatives

Special Offer/Incentive:
A 20% discount voucher for bookings during the week (i.e. excluding Friday-Sunday). Cannot be combined with any other special offer, discount or promotion.

★ **20% DISCOUNT** (see text)
Please mention Direct Experiences when booking

Great Central Railway

Britain's only double-track, fully signalled, main line heritage steam railway. Imagine the thrill of taking control of a living and breathing steam engine. It's the stuff of childhood dreams. We have three experience packages to choose from.

Activity Location:
Midlands

Contact Details:
Great Central Railway plc
T: 01509 230726
E: sales@gcrailway.co.uk
W: www.gcrailway.co.uk

Practical Information:
All packages start at Loughborough, Leicestershire
Participants must be 18 years or over and fit
All equipment supplied

Availability:
Open all year

Corporates:
Suitable for corporate events

Special Offer/Incentive:
Exclusive to this book £50.00 off Silver and Gold voucher. Please quote U/E 06. Cannot be combined with any other special offer, discount or promotion.

★ **£50 DISCOUNT** (see text)
When you quote REF: U/E 06

Experiences:

Bronze:
For complete novices. Take control of an engine without carriages for a 16-mile round trip shared with another driver. Enjoy lunch on the train and a tour of the railway. The whole family can come along for a fun day out.

Silver:
You'll be driving an engine complete with the train of carriages (your family can ride while you drive) over the 32 miles shared with another driver. Sample the signal box, delve behind the scenes in the engine shed and have lunch on us.

Gold:
The ultimate driving experience – 64 fantastic footplate miles and a train that is yours for the day. As close as you can get to living as a hero from the age of steam. Lunch included.

Now if you'd prefer something a little more modern we have a fine fleet of heritage diesels at the railway ... Driving packages to suit all pockets and tastes are available. Ask for details.

Meadow Farm Studio

Meadow Farm Studio is a professional recording studio, situated in the Derbyshire countryside, with over 40 years of experience in the recording/music profession.

Experiences:

The Recording Experience:

This experience provides a unique chance of becoming the new recording sensation, with numerous backing tracks to choose from. The session is on a one-to-one basis and provides an opportunity to see the work that goes on in any recording studio.

You'll be in the capable hands of a qualified, experienced engineer/producer to guide you through the recording process; vocal guidance is given throughout the session with a 'voice training manual' included.

The 1- and 2-hour sessions are ideal for a solo or duet, and the longer sessions can be used by up to four people - this could include a band/group to record that all important demo.

Other Experiences:

- *The Instrumentalist.* Instead of vocals you play the instrument in this session, e.g. drums, guitar (contact studio for further details)
- *The Engineer.* A 'hands-on' experience, record your own material or from material previously recorded
- *The Corporate.* Four hours studio time for up to ten people, for either separate or combined performances
- *Hen or Stag.* Three hours studio time for up to ten people, for either separate or combined performances

Activity Location:
Midlands

Contact Details:
Meadow Farm Studio
T: 01773 740264
E: stewart@MeadowFarmStudio.co.uk
W: www.meadowfarmstudio.co.uk

Gift Vouchers:
Personalised gift vouchers range from 1 hour 'taster' sessions to 12 hour recording sessions

Additional Information:
For all Corporate, Hen & Stag events, Derek Jason (ex lead singer 'Rockin Berries') will be on hand for additional coaching (subject to availability)

Special Offer:
A 10% discount is available with this publication. Please mention Direct Experiences when booking. Cannot be combined with any other special offers, discounts or promotions.

★ **10% DISCOUNT** Please mention Direct Experiences when booking

Star Listings International

Star Listings International is an established and respected company that provide a star naming service. If someone has a special place in your heart why not give them a special place in the universe? We register your chosen name and its unique astronomical co-ordinates in our copyrighted register, creating a timeless present for today and the future.

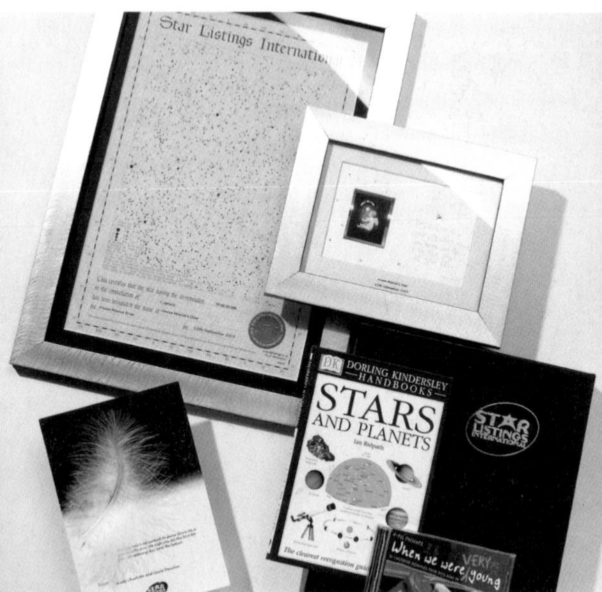

Ordering Information:
Star Listings International
T: 01455 845541
E: help@starlistings.co.uk
W: www.starlistings.co.uk

- Size of the combined certificate and Star Chart is A3 size, approximately 42 × 30cm
- Duplicate certificates can be purchased
- Allow 2–3 days for Express delivery or 21 days for standard delivery
- We guarantee we will not register any star twice

Please note that naming a star for someone is a stunning and unique gift, but your star name will not be used or recognised by the astronomic or scientific community, and no legal title is inferred or implied

Special Offer/Incentive:
Quote DE06 on ordering to receive a 10% discount. Cannot be combined with any other special offers, discounts or promotions.

★ 10% DISCOUNT
When you quote REF: DE06

Experiences:

Standard Gift Set:
This comprises:

- A combined Certificate of Registration and an A3 Star Chart Scroll, showing the exact location of the named star with astronomical co-ordinates
- Complimentary messaging service
- An attractive presentation pack

Deluxe Gift Pack:
This comprises:

- A combined Certificate of Registration and an A3 Star Chart Scroll, showing the exact location of the named star with astronomical co-ordinates
- A handmade picture that is tailor-made to the occasion, also showing your star name
- A copy of the best selling Dorling Kindersley *Stars and Planets* book
- A CD of specially chosen music, also suitable for the occasion
- Complimentary messaging service
- All packaged in an attractive presentation gift box

Deluxe Gift Pack with framed Star Chart:
As above with the Star Chart beautifully framed.

This is a truly once-in-a-lifetime gift that will shine forever.

Reilly Studios

Reilly Studios is an award-winning photography studio, based in Leicestershire, boasting over 30 years' experience in the industry.

We pride ourselves on being one step ahead when it comes to producing both modern and contemporary photographic art, together with pioneering products for displaying in your homes.

Our aim is to give you a memorable, fun experience.

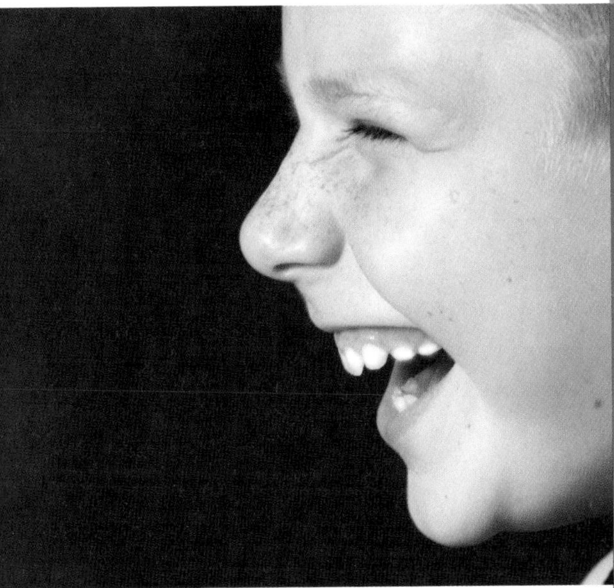

Experiences:

Reilly Studios Makeover & Family Portrait Experiences - The collections.

Elementary Collection:
An opportunity to sample our photography in our professional studio. From the photograph of your choice we will produce a framed desktop portrait as a keepsake.

Little Angels Collection:
Touch the hearts of many, have your children and/or pets character and soul captured in a wall portrait displayed in a product of your choice.

Family Collection:
Bring your family together to capture your unique bond in a timeless wall portrait. Your images can be framed, placed on canvas or displayed in an album as a timeless memory.

Ultimate Collection:
You decide who you bring to our studio: Pets, family, children or loved ones. We will then individually design a unique album, together with a wall product of your choice.

Makeover Collection:
A unique opportunity to be pampered and look your best! We will then capture a collection of images from which we will create a unique, individually designed album.

Activity Location:
Midlands

Contact Details:
Reilly Studios
T: 01455 610782
E: Info@reillystudios.co.uk
W: www.reillystudios.co.uk

Practical Information:
Bring a selection of casual and formal outfits
Bring a selection of toys and treats for pets and children
Min. age for makeovers is 16 years

Gift Vouchers:
Available from £75

Appointments:
Tuesday and Wednesday 9am-7pm
Friday 9am-5pm
Saturday and Sunday 9am-5pm

Special Offer/Incentive:
Special offer for 2006: All portrait sittings included in each package price will be charged at only £10 (normally £45) and donated to Leicester Animal Aid charity. (Charity number 242560).

Mid Wales Shooting Centre

Mid Wales Shooting Centre has established itself as one of the premier clay target facilities in the UK. Situated in 300 acres and surrounded by naturally beautiful countryside, we are ideally located 1 hour's drive from the Midlands. We cater for the novice to the expert shooter, providing a vast range of shooting facilities, sporting, skeet and trap.

Activity Location:
Wales

Contact Details:
Mid Wales Shooting Centre
T: 0870 896 4764
E: enquiries@midwalesshootingcentre.com
W: www.midwalesshootingcentre.com

Availability:
Open Mon–Sat (9–5.30) and 2nd and 4th Sundays in the month

Practical Information:
All equipment is available for hire at the venue

Special Offer/Incentive:
A 10% discount is available to readers (excluding gun purchases). Cannot be combined with any other special offer, discount or promotion.

Experiences:

- *Instruction.* We have professional instructors on hand to help you reach your full potential at all levels, from the novice through to the experienced shooter. Also available are master classes for all clay shooting disciplines and game with Peter Croft
- *Short Breaks.* These can be arranged by appointment – please call for details and availability
- *Established Centre.* Over the past 10 years the centre has played host to World, British, Welsh, and English championships and is host to the world famous Krieghoff 500 classic
- *Corporate Hospitality.* Mid Wales Shooting Centre offers the perfect corporate hospitality entertainment set in some of the finest and naturally beautiful countryside in the British Isles. Catering for up to 50 guests. Shooting groups are kept small with each group having its own experienced instructor. Our large shooting lodge overlooks the shooting ranges and is an ideal setting for buffets or full three-course meals
- *Facilities.* In the centre of the grounds stands a superb log timber clubhouse/restaurant and an extensive shop offering a huge range of guns, clothing and accessories

★ **10% DISCOUNT** (see text)
Please mention Direct Experiences when booking

GreenLight Performance Bike Hire

Much more than just bike hire

Our customers are able to hire top-range performance motorcycles manufactured by Suzuki, Honda and Yamaha. All GreenLight motorcycles are late registration and come with the latest security tagging systems and/or DatatoolTM. Our expert customer care staff will ensure you have the correct knowledge and equipment for a thoroughly enjoyable experience.

Activity Location:
West Midlands

Contact Details:
Greenlight Performance Bike Hire
T: 0845 1300 718
E: info@greenlightbikes.co.uk
W: www.greenlightbikes.co.uk

Practical Information:
Minimum age restrictions apply to each bike, and a full bike licence is required
All safety equipment can be hired on site
Daily, weekend or weekly rates available

Special Offer/Incentive:
A 10% discount is available when you mention this publication. Cannot be combined with any other special offers, discounts or promotions.

Experiences:

Choose from our latest models – these include:

- Suzuki 600 Bandit
- Suzuki GSXR 600
- Honda CBR 1000 RR
- Suzuki SV 1000
- Suzuki SV 650S
- Suzuki GSXR 1000
- Yamaha YZF R6
- Honda CG 125

We are able to offer tried and tested exciting routes for customers who are looking for a memorable journey on great roads used by motorcyclists. Just ask when you collect your machine.

We can service road and off-road motorcycles and have a fast ordering service for parts and accessories. See our website for full and further information.

We also have a large range of protective clothing for hire, these include boots, gloves, jackets, trousers, one-piece suits and the all-important helmets.

★ **10% DISCOUNT** Please mention *Ultimate Gift Experiences* when booking

Haimwood Sporting Limited

Haimwood Sporting Ground is a superb riverside venue in Llandrinio, Powys, offering a range of outdoor activities to test your skill and provide exciting entertainment. Expert tuition is on hand for all levels of ability including complete beginners.

Activity Location:
Wales

Contact Details:
Haimwood Sporting Limited
T: 01 691 830 764
E: enquiries@haimwood.com
W: www.haimwood.com

Availability:
Open all year round

Practical Information:
Local accommodation is available upon request

Special Offer/Incentive:
A 10% discount is available to readers. Cannot be combined with any other discounts or promotional offers.

★ **10% DISCOUNT** Please mention *Ultimate Gift Experiences* when booking

Experiences:

- *Shooting*: Why not try your skills on our long and short range?
- *Canoeing*: Kayaks or Canadian (open). Learn the skills from the experts. Get the feel of the river
- *Raft Building*: Be part of a team using just a few basic materials to make a safe and stable floating platform. Then the really exciting bit, launch the craft and put it to the test
- *Archery*: This time-honoured sport takes years to master. But you'll be amazed at what you can achieve in just a short time with expert tuition
- *4x4 Off-Road Driving*: Our off-road course has been been designed to test your judgement and driving ability
- *Team Building*: We have available a number of exercises, both mental and physical. These can be used to test and build team spirit
- *Fishing*: On the River Seven, mainly coarse, but there are some salmon and trout
- *Model Aero Flying*: Dual control, circuits, aerobatics, no parachute necessary
- *Clay Target Shooting*: Professional tuition available for novices and first timers. Try this most exciting country sport at a premier shooting ground

Plus many off-site activities such as paragliding, white-water rafting, abseiling and rock climbing, paint ball and quad trekking

A Tree 4 You

If someone you know deserves a place in history, then you've already taken the first step towards giving him or her the present of a lifetime. At A Tree 4 You, we are offering you the opportunity to buy a baby tree that is in a recyclable transparent tube.

Location:
Nationwide

Contact Details:
A Tree 4 You
E: sales@sayitwithatree.co.uk
W: www.sayitwithatree.co.uk

Special Offer/Incentive:
A 10% discount is available to readers. Please quote ref. DE06.

Experiences:

Buy A Tree:
You can give someone special a unique novelty gift that will grow forever. We have a range of beautiful gift packs available suitable for Valentine's Day, birthdays, christenings, anniversaries, weddings, Christmas gifts and lots more.

All of our gift packs contain a Scots Pine (*Pinus sylvestris*) in a beautiful presentation box complete with personalised message card.

You can also add to your gift with any or all of the following (at an additional charge):

- A children's tree activity pack
- DK *Book of Trees* (250 colour pages) containing details of all types of trees
- CD of relaxing music

Corporate Gifts:
We can offer an appropriate tree to suit your needs. All of our trees are grown from seed, which is sourced from sustainable forests and gathered with either the Forestry Commission or the National Trust.

Once grown to a suitable size our trees are presented (unless otherwise requested) in a clear tube with an option of bespoke labelling. We can offer direct mail services or supply bulk packed to a central location: whatever your needs we will endeavour to create your perfect promotion.

★ **10% DISCOUNT**
When you quote REF: DE06

Short courses

'What a splendid thing watercolour is to express atmosphere and distance, so that the figure is surrounded by air and can breathe in it.'

VINCENT VAN GOGH

A learning experience

A day at a flower academy is as good a way as any of getting a glimpse into a more beautiful world. Flower decorations go far beyond the garden borders; and subjects such as wedding flowers, dinner party decorations and bouquets can help you expand a love of all things floral into other areas of your life.

The beauty of it is that it's not just about what you feel on the day. You can take what you've learnt and continue to apply it to your everyday life.

Similarly a watercolour course manages to be both therapeutic and a learning experience. Courses can either be on general techniques or specific subjects. The latter lean heavily towards the rural landscapes or country churches end of things, rather than gasworks or landfills so the whole experience is intended to be soothing as well as educational.

Each session begins with a demonstration then students get to work on their own paintings with one-on-one guidance tailored to individual needs. Because it's a one-on-one affair courses can normally accommodate anyone from beginner level to RA wannabe so grab your great big floppy straw hat and give it a go.

Photography courses will follow a similar pattern, with a talk on techniques followed by a photo-taking outing with the tutor on hand to advise. Courses may focus on specific types of subject matter so pick the one that interests you most, from landscapes to portraits and everything in between.

A basic wine-tasting course will not only cover tasting and choosing wines but also help you with tips on storing and serving. More advanced courses may focus on particular regions, wine styles, classic vintages and matching wines with food. You'll be provided with a certificate at the end of the course so that you can prove to everyone that you're now a connoisseur.

If you're suffering from writer's block then a writing course could be just what you need. Often located in inspirational surroundings, these courses provide expert tuition and constructive criticism from a team of professional writers. You'll also get the chance to swap tips and share problems with other wannabe J.K. Rowlings and John Grishams. Courses will often focus on specific aspects of writing such as poetry, screenwriting or writing for children, so you can choose a course that caters exactly for your needs.

For a more active learning experience why not try a dance or Pilates course? Whether it's a short intensive course or a slower, more long-term series of lessons you're after, there'll be something to cater for your needs. Suitable for adults and children of all abilities, these courses could help you unlock a hidden terpsichorean talent, so get your tights on and plié away.

Rebecca Hind

Tuition in traditional English watercolour painting.

Activity Location:
South East

Contact Details:
Rebecca Hind
E: post@rebeccahind.com
W: www.rebeccahind.com

Practical Information:
Min. age 16 yrs
Classes held at beautiful locations in rural Oxfordshire, with good company! Access varies between venues but is generally good

Availability:
Please see website for further information www.rebeccahind.com

Special Offer/Incentive:
A 10% discount is available to groups of five or more enrolling on the same course.

Experiences:

Enjoyable tuition in watercolour painting from a professional artist and teacher of adults.

These non-residential classes are held in ten week terms, weekends and summer schools throughout South Oxfordshire. Locations vary seasonally and are held indoors or out accordingly.

Teaching is by demonstration and one-to-one, with reference to the Master of British watercolours. Your class will be run by an experienced tutor in small classes, allowing for optimum tutor/student ratio and visibility during demonstrations.

The teaching includes stretching paper, choosing a subject, tonality, colour theory, composition, perspective, laying washes, drawing and more, in a variety of subject matter.

★ **10% DISCOUNT** For groups of five or more enrolling on the same course

The Simon Lycett Flower Academy

An opportunity to learn even more tricks of the trade! At his Flower Academy in South London Simon Lycett, the celebrity floral decorator whose clients include Elton John, HM the Queen and the Beckhams, offers one-day courses that are full of sensational designs. Classes cover a variety of useful and interesting subjects such as 'dinner party decorations', 'flowers in the garden' and 'wedding flowers'.

Activity Location:
South London

Contact Details:
Simon Lycett Flower Academy
T: 0870 240 4063
E: floweracademy@simonlycett.co.uk
W: www.simonlycett.co.uk

Availability:
Please contact us for a brochure containing dates and an application form or book online
Classes run throughout the Spring/Summer and Autumn/Winter months

Gift vouchers:
Treat someone to their ultimate experience of a day's flower arranging!

Corporate/Groups:
Let us tailor make that special day for you for that celebratory occasion! Maximum 15

Special Offer/Incentive:
A 10% discount is available. Please state code UGE2006 when booking. Cannot be combined with any other special offer, discount or promotion.

★ 10% DISCOUNT
When you quote REF: UGE2006

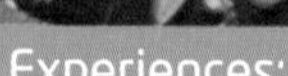

Experiences:

From the smash hit film *Four Weddings and a Funeral*, Simon's floral creations have appeared regularly on the big screen. He also features on television as 'Floral Expert' and 'Style Guru'. Simon's work has taken him to famous venues all over the world where he has created amazing floral decorations for world leaders (President Bush), celebrities (for David and Victoria Beckham's wedding, Simon created a fairytale setting in Ireland) and several royal families (Simon was invited back to Windsor Castle to decorate the wedding of HRH Prince Charles to HRH the Duchess of Cornwall).

Pupils are encouraged to stretch their imagination and explore the realms of possibility. Classes begin at 10.00am with coffee and biscuits followed by a demonstration which pupils then copy. After a delicious lunch accompanied by carefully selected chilled wines, hands-on learning again follows the afternoon demonstration as pupils replicate their own version.

At 3.30pm the day concludes when pupils take home, in addition to their two fabulous arrangements, a head full of ideas, a folder full of facts and one of Simon's complimentary books packed with techniques and inspiration.

'The course was perfectly planned, allowing time for each student to produce two impressive arrangements and for us to quiz Simon on his insider secrets over a delicious lunch.' – Miranda Watchorn, *Homes & Gardens*.

The Place

The Place is the UK's premier centre for contemporary dance, uniting training, creation and performance in one unique building.

The programme of courses provides the very best teaching in contemporary dance, Pilates and ballet at all ability levels.

Activity Location:
London

Contact Details:
The Place
T: 0207 1211000(admin & general enquiries)
E: info@theplace.org.uk
W: www.theplace.org.uk

Gift Vouchers:
Gift vouchers can be redeemed against termly bookings or drop-in prices for any evening classes and short courses. Vouchers are fully transferable and make the ideal gift for experienced dancers or absolute beginners

Additional Information:
The Place has an on-line shop, where educational DVDs and videos can be purchased as well as gift vouchers

Experiences:

Short Courses

Summer Intensives includes an exciting weekly programme of five-day courses. Run by dance professionals, all sharing their experiences and skills in a series of technique classes, repertory and creative workshops.

Summer Intensives also include ballet classes for all abilities, as well as yoga, Pilates and physical theatre with all classes being accompanied by live music.

The programme provides real choice for all dancers whether you are near professional level or just starting out.

Photography Courses at Dimbola Lodge Museum

The aim of the trust is to ensure the preservation of Dimbola Lodge and to provide historical information on Julia Margaret Cameron's life and works. Julia Margaret Cameron lived at Dimbola Lodge from 1860 until 1875, where she photographed the cream of Victorian Society. We also ensure an extensive list of activities, events and exhibitions take place in and around Dimbola Lodge Museum to support the trust and to support photographers from all over the world.

Activity Location:
Isle of Wight

Contact Details:
Nicky Dabbs
Dimbola Lodge Museum
T: 01983 756814
E: nicky@dimbola.freeserve.co.uk
W: www.dimbola.co.uk

Practical Information:
Courses suit beginners up to advanced
Children's workshops also available
All courses are non-residential although there is plenty of good-quality accommodation nearby

Special Offer/Incentive:
Course subsidies are available for young people, people on a low income and people with disabilities

Experiences:

An important part of the Trust's role includes that of education and its main aim is to create an enjoyable experience available to all. All workshops are managed by Dimbola Lodge Museum's Learning and Access Officer, who is funded by the Isle of Wight Economic Partnership through the Leader+ programme. This year a programme has been arranged to appeal to everyone from the beginner to the advanced and includes modules for digital and film. We offer a personalised service to schools, interest groups and individual students.

Cameron's work is celebrated in the range of photography courses that Dimbola offers to both amateurs and professionals. Courses include wildlife, landscape, computer, darkroom, pinhole, studio and masterclasses with world-renowned photographers in their field.

[Main photo: *Tennyson Down* by tutor John Walker.]

Berry Bros. & Rudd

World renowned wine merchant Berry Bros. & Rudd offers a wide range of wine courses at its 17th-century premises in St James's Street, London. The beautifully restored cellars date back to 1698 and the shopfront is one of the few 18th-century examples surviving in London.

Activity Location:
Greater London

Contact Details:
Berry Bros. & Rudd Wine School
T: 0870 900 4300
W: www.bbr.com

Practical Information:
The focus is the *practical* aspects of enjoying wine via evening classes
Maximum class size of 36 people ensures *individual attention*
Many wines are tasted blind to make learning both *interactive* and fun
Course folder with notes provided
Berry Bros. & Rudd *Certificate* when the course is completed
Six sessions per course with start times throughout the year

Experiences:

Introductory Wine Course:
- Basic *tasting techniques*
- Choosing from a restaurant wine list
- Tasting the major grape varieties
- Laying wines down
- Serving tips and techniques
- Discovering your favourite styles of wine and why

Classic Wine Regions Course:
- *Key characteristics* of the principal wine regions
- Interesting *alternatives to classics*
- Key producers in different regions
- *Terroir*, an international concept?
- Influence of grape variety
- Importance of vintage
- *Classification systems*: a helpful guide or hindrance?
- Matching different styles of *wine with food*

Berrys' Bordeaux & Burgundy Course:
Tutored by Jasper Morris MW and Mark Pardoe MW, this course focuses on France's most famous wine regions, Bordeaux and Burgundy.
- Terroir
- Styles of wines produced
- Classifying the concept of quality
- Identifying value within the regions
- Alternatives to the best known names
- Key producers
- New and future developments
- Laying down wines/analysing ability to age
- Buying En Primeur

Felicity Fair Thompson - Writing Workshops

Felicity Fair Thompson has a Masters degree in Screenwriting from London College of Communication. Her published work includes fiction, poetry, scenic travel features for magazines. She writes and directs travel films. She teaches short film, and fiction and creative writing for young people and for Adult Education.

Activity Location:
Isle of Wight

Contact Details:
Felicity Fair Thompson
T: 01983 407772
E: felicity@writeplot.co.uk
W: www.writeplot.co.uk

Practical Information:
Courses last between 3 and 5 days
Suitable for beginners, intermediates and advanced writers
Residential and non residential
Group size 1-7

Special Offer/Incentive:
A 10% cash back discount is available on production of this book on arrival.

★ **10% CASH BACK DISCOUNT**
When this book is produced on arrival

Experiences:

Writing Holidays:
Isn't it time to make a real breakthrough with your work?

Overall we concentrate on fiction in the form of the novel and writing for children as well as other fiction forms – expanding the way you write prose, and drawing on your own experience.

Take the chance to make real progress and leap your work forward, with five days' individual help and workshopping. Find new ways with words, develop your story and discover the power of structure, theme, genre and tone. There is individual time to work on your own writing project – the opportunity for shared discussion with a small group of other holidaying writers – and the freedom to enjoy the Island in a stylish home-from-home setting.

Weekend Script Clinic:
The programme includes individual work on your own script and group workshops looking at structure, theme, tone, setting and characters and how key scenes of dialogue are progressing the plot.

Profile Writer

On a profile writer course you will learn about modern day internet dating and the great way to promote yourself both on and off-line. We'll show you how to describe yourself so that it emits an accurate impression and attracts genuine, interesting people.

Location:
Midlands

Contact Details:
Profile Writer
T: 07833 567 300
E: info@profile-writer.co.uk
W: www.profile-writer.co.uk

Availability:
Spaces are limited and the demand is high, so please book early to avoid disappointment
Evening and weekend courses are available

Practical information:
Participants must be over 18 years

Special Offer/Incentive:
A 10% discount is available to readers. Cannot be combined with any other special offer, discount or promotion.

Experiences:

During the half day course we cover such topics as:

- Realistic expectations from Internet dating
- 5 steps to dating heaven
- Writing a great profile to sell yourself
- Getting a great photograph
- What do I say next?
- Danger signs and how to avoid difficult situations
- Bailing out on a first date
- Creating the right image for you

We will give you the tools to write a fresh, up-beat and stimulating profile, investigate why Internet dating is such a great way of meeting your ideal partner and also inform you of some of the pitfalls you are likely to find along the way. During the session our writers will be on hand to give plenty of creative writing help and advice. Although you will not be given the opportunity to join a dating site, you will be given the confidence to step into cyberspace dating or renew your faith that a potential partner is only a click away.

★ **10% DISCOUNT** Please mention *Ultimate Gift Experiences* when booking

Plain Sailing

Welcome to Plain Sailing. We offer RYA Training courses in sailing, motorboats and powerboats, along with all one day RYA (Royal Yachting Association) courses. We have a wide range of yachts, motorboats and powerboats on the fleet available for fun days out, training, skippered and bareboat charter, while operating on the beautiful coast of South Devon in Brixham.

Activity Location:
South West

Contact Details:
Plain Sailing
T: 01803 853843
E: enquiries@plainsailing.co.uk
W: www.plainsailing.co.uk

Availability:
Open year round

Prices:
Full course content and prices can be found on our comprehensive website

Equipment:
A full kit list will be issued upon booking

Special Offer/Incentive:
A 5% discount is available to readers. Cannot be combined with any other special offer, discount or promotion.

★ **5% DISCOUNT** Please mention *Ultimate Gift Experiences* when booking

Experiences:

- *RYA Sailing Courses.* Our courses will improve your sailing skills to a level recognised by the Royal Yachting Association, in a relaxed and enjoyable atmosphere. There can be no better place to start your holiday or training than the scenic and picturesque South West Coast or the beautiful and sunny Portuguese coast
  We run training and sailing all year round, to suit all abilities from beginners to Yachtmaster Ocean plus cruises in UK and foreign waters for individuals and family groups
- *RYA Motor Boat Training.* We have a series of courses designed for the complete beginner from leisure to Offshore Yachtmaster's with commercial endorsements. The shore-based courses are run in our purpose built classroom situated on the marina. Practical training takes place on board the twin-engine Motor Cruisers
- *RYA Power Boat Training.* The RYA National Power Boat Scheme provides recognised levels of training for the complete beginner, wishing to take full advantage of their rib or sports boat in a safe leisurely environment, up to advanced and specialist driving skills with commercial endorsement
- *The Round Britain Experience.* This is a well-established training and adventure programme that has been finely tuned to provide one of the best sailing experiences in the world. We are now offering our expertise to organisations, companies and individuals who may be interested in using the experience as a platform for their own ideas

More course and details are available on our website.

Days out

'Wherever the wind takes me
I travel as a visitor.'
HORACE, ROMAN POET

Away days

In our busy modern lives we can often find weekends filled up with work, DIY and shopping, while holidays seem few and far between. So here are a few reminders of why it's important to take time and make weekends special again. Whether you need to find something to keep the children occupied on a rainy Saturday or during school holidays, or simply want to add some excitement to your own day off, there's a thrilling day out to be found here.

Heroes and villains

An excellent family day out can be had by visiting one of the many castles – from ruins to stately homes – that dot our countryside. Many of them lay on tours, games and events aimed specifically at children, but are interesting places rich in history to be enjoyed by people of all ages. If you get a chance to go to one of the jousting events organised at some castles you'll be transported back in time to the age of chivalry and get to see exactly what being a knight was all about. If you want to find out what happened to the bad guys in days gone by then take a trip to the ghoulish delights of a tour round a dungeon, complete with terrifically terrifying re-enactments of the dungeon's history – sensationally scary.

Arts and crafts

Art-lovers are well catered for when it comes to day trips. Browsing round galleries of paintings and sculptures is a relaxing way to spend a few hours and children can get involved and kept interested with quizzes and art-related activities. Pottery museums give you a great chance to see the history of this industry, find out how your crockery is made and buy something to take away with you as a souvenir of your day. For a fascinating glimpse of how our taste in home décor has evolved over the centuries take a look at a museum of interior design. Who knows, you may come away with a few tips and ideas for your own home the next time you get stuck with a DIY weekend.

Out of this world

If you've exhausted all the day trips planet Earth has to offer then it's time to take a trip into outer space. Learn the history of space exploration and even experience the thrill of being an astronaut in a simulated exploration of space. Adults and children will all find this a fascinating and stimulating day to remember.

Mallory Park Circuit

Mallory Park is a great place, a special place to many people. Spectators, competitors, officials and more.

Why? It's difficult to say but probably an amalgam of many factors. Races won... races lost ... speed ... action ... excitement ... history... Different things to different people.

Experiences:

What is true is that Mallory Park offers spectators a great variety of exciting motor sport events every weekend during the racing season. Motorcycles or cars, new or old. Something for every true motor sport enthusiast. Plenty of places for spectators to get really close to the action ... plenty of places for competitors to overtake.

And of course its not just about racing ... at other times you can drive or ride around the very same circuit as competitors do ... enjoying the sensations of high speed without the need to worry about traffic, speed limits or your licence!

You will find a complete diary of events on our website www.mallorypark.co.uk

Mallory Park is the perfect location for hospitality, catering for individual groups or corporate clients from 2 to 175 people or more. Product launches, trade exhibitions, corporate entertaining, sales meetings, conferencing, etc., why not make Mallory your venue with a difference!

General Testing Days are held every Wednesday throughout the year for cars and motorcycles (please phone for details).

Limited number of places available. Advanced booking essential.

We hope that you will join us at Mallory Park – we know you will enjoy it ...

Activity Location:
Midlands

Contact Details:
Mallory Race Circuit
T: 01455 842931
E: info@mallorypark.co.uk
W: www.mallorypark.co.uk

Practical Information:
Admission charges vary depending on event
Parking *free* of charge at all meetings. Use the park n view areas to watch from the comfort of your own car
Children aged 15 and under are admitted *free* of charge to all meetings
Catering outlets located around the circuit offering hot and cold snacks
No animals admitted except guide dogs

Tickets:
Admission is always available at the gate or in advance on the web site or from:
Phone: 01455 842931 (09.00–17.00, Monday to Friday)
E-mail: tickets@mallorypark.co.uk

Special Offer:
A minimum 10% discount is available when booking tickets in advance. Please mention Direct Experiences when booking. Cannot be combined with any other special offer, discount or promotion.

★ 10% DISCOUNT
Please mention Direct Experiences when booking

Pembrey Circuit

Located in south west Wales the Pembrey circuit is often referred to as the Welsh Motor Sport Centre offering a wide variety of events apart from traditional circuit racing. As one of the newer venues in British motor sport the circuit offers a wide range of challenges to the competitor with an assortment of bends and corners.

Activity Location:
South West Wales

Contact Details:
Pembrey Circuit
T: 01554 891042
W: www.barc.net

Special Offers:
Contact circuit for further details.

Experiences:

- Great family day out with good viewing available
- Range of events to suit all interests:
  - Club car racing
  - Club motorcycle racing
  - Truck racing
  - Rallycross
  - Single venue stage rallies
  - Sprints
- On site catering and bar facilities
- Prices from only £10 per adult
- Children 16 and under admitted free of charge
- Free parking

Thruxton Circuit

Located on the A303 to the west of Andover, Thruxton is the home of the British Automobile Racing Club. Having remained unchanged from its original layout it is currently the fastest race circuit in the United Kingdom, which consistently provides some of the very best racing available. Thruxton hosts rounds of all of the major national championships for motorcycles and cars.

Activity Location:
South West

Contact Details:
Thruxton Circuit
T: 01264 882200
W: www.barc.net

Special Offers:
Book in advance and save up to 20%.

Experiences:

- Great family day out with good viewing available
- Range of events to suit all interests:
  - British Superbikes
  - British Touring Cars
  - Formula Three
  - British Truck Racing
  - Club Racing
  - Grandstand seating available
- On-site catering and bar facilities
- Prices from only £10 per adult
- Children 16 and under admitted free of charge
- Free parking

★ **UP TO 20% DISCOUNT**
When booked in advance

The Dungeons

Incorporating the famous London Dungeon as well as UK sites in York and Edinburgh. Featuring live actors, special effects, interactive exhibits and chilling rides, the dungeons bring the country's most horrible history vividly back to life!

Activity Location:
London, North East and Scotland

Contact Details:
The London Dungeon
T: 0207 403 7221
The York Dungeon
T: 01904 632599
The Edinburgh Dungeon
T: 0131 240 1000
www.thedungeons.com

Practical Information:
The Dungeons have disabled access
The Dungeons are not recommended for those of a nervous disposition or very young children. Children must be accompanied by an adult

Groups:
We welcome large groups or school parties. Contact us for further details and preferential rates 0207 403 7221 (option 2)

Special Offer/Incentive:
Quote 'Direct Experiences' at the cash desk to receive a great 20% discount for entry to any of the three UK Dungeons! Cannot be combined with any other special offer, discount or promotion.

★ 20% DISCOUNT
Please quote 'Direct Experiences' at cash desk

Experiences:

At the *London Dungeon* you will come face to face with some of the most infamous villains and gruesome events of the capital's history. Feel the fear as you are taken through the dark, dank passages of London's scariest attraction which includes:

- A rendezvous with a sadistic torturer in his chamber of horrors
- A stroll to visit the doctor in London's plague ravished streets
- A date with destiny with an eccentric and brutal 18th century judge who will delight in sending you to you death on the chilling Traitor: Boat Ride to Hell!
- Going on the trail of London's most notorious serial killer – Jack the Ripper!
- Escaping the smoke and flames of the Great Fire of London
- *New for 2006!* Need a hair cut? Let's hope so as you will be visiting the shop of London's notorious Demon Barber – the sick and murderous Sweeney Todd!

For horrible history a little closer to home try the *York* and *Edinburgh* Dungeons where the pain and fear continue – with a uniquely local twist!

Rockingham Castle

450 years a royal castle and 450 years a family home. A visit to Rockingham Castle is a fascinating journey through the evolution of a building from Norman fortress to English country home.

Activity Location:
Midlands

Contact Details:
Rockingham Castle
T: 01536 770240
E: estateoffice@rockinghamcastle.com
W: www.rockinghamcastle.com

Practical Information:
Most areas of the house and gardens are accessible to disabled visitors
Audio tours are available

Opening Times:
Easter to end of May – Sundays and Bank Holiday Mondays
June to September – Tuesdays, Sundays and Bank Holiday Mondays
Grounds open at 12 noon and close at 4.30pm
Castle opens at 1pm and close at 5pm

Special Offer/Incentive:
A £1 discount is available on every castle and grounds ticket. – please quote *Ultimate Gift Experiences*. Cannot be combined with any other special offer, discount or promotion.

Experiences:

- *The Normans.* With its magnificent views across the Welland Valley, the castle was crucial in helping William the Conqueror subdue his new kingdom
- *Medieval Period.* Many medieval kings came to Rockingham Castle, Richard the Lion Heart played host to his Scottish counterpart here and his unpopular brother John came frequently to hunt in Rockingham Forest. John then left his treasure chest in the Great Hall, giving rise to the legend that his crown jewels are buried at Rockingham
- *Tudors.* Henry VIII granted the castle to Edward Watson, who converted the medieval fortress into a comfortable Tudor house
- *Civil War.* Originally a Royalist stronghold, Rockingham Castle was taken by Cromwell's Roundheads and then besieged by the King's troops
- *Victorians.* Rockingham was in its heyday as a Victorian mansion, filled with Richard and Lavina Watson's family friends and servants
- *Contemporary Rockingham.* The castle remains the centre of a community and is the home of the Saunders Watson family, direct descendents of Edward Watson
- *Gardens.* Poised above the Welland Valley with fine views of five counties, the ramparts enclose 12 acres of sweeping lawns, formal and informal gardens set among medieval fortifications

★ **£1 DISCOUNT** on every castle and grounds ticket (quote *Ultimate Gift Experiences*)

Belvoir Castle

Enjoy a superb day out at Belvoir Castle – with beautiful views, glorious gardens and a fascinating magical castle to explore. There's something for everyone at Belvoir.

Activity Location:
Midlands

Contact Details:
Belvoir Castle
T: 01476 871002
E: info@belvoircastle.com
W: www.belvoircastle .com

Availability:
In 2006 we're open 11am–5pm from 1 April until 30 September. Closed Mondays and Fridays. Open Bank Holiday Mondays. Please call to check opening times for the day you wish to visit

Special Offer/Incentive:
A 10% discount is available to readers of *Ultimate Gift Experiences.* Cannot be combined with any other special offer, discount or promotion.

★ **10% DISCOUNT** Please mention *Ultimate Gift Experiences* when booking

Experiences:

The magnificent castle commands splendid views over the Vale of Belvoir.

Your visit could includethe following.

- *A Superb Guided Tour*: During the week free guided tours are available at 12.30pm and 2.30pm
- *Costume Guides and Re-enactments*: Our guides are often in costume and, on selected weekends, perform re-enactments including the trial of the Belvoir Witches
- *Children's Activities*: As well as an adventure playground and children's quiz, you'll enjoy the delightful Regency Nursery and School Room
- *Beautiful Gardens & Grounds featuring*: The Rose Garden – replanted in 2002 and leading down to the Cibber statues
- *The Duchess's Spring Garden* – a fine example of a Victorian valley garden, with many rare species of trees as well as an Edwardian rare daffodil collection
- *The Queen's Royal Lancers Museum*: Following the story of the Queen's Royal Lancers from their formation to the present day. This intriguing museum includes arms, uniforms, painting and artefacts
- *Park Events*: Events take place in the park and castle every weekend throughout the summer
- *Special Occasions*: Belvoir is the perfect setting for your special wedding day – we are licensed for both civil and religious ceremonies
- *Corporate Functions*: Whether a small seminar or a major product launch

Salford Museum & Art Gallery

There's lots to see and do! Stroll down our Victorian Street, Lark Hill Place or relax amidst the splendour of our Victorian Gallery. With an ever-changing temporary exhibition programme, from hands-on activities to modern art, there's always something going on at Salford Museum and Art Gallery!

Activity Location:
North West

Contact Details:
Salford Museum & Art Gallery
T: 0161 778 0800
E: Salford.museum@salford.gov.uk
W: www.salford.gov.uk/museums

Opening Times:
Monday-Friday 10am-4.45pm
Sat/Sun 1pm-5pm
The museum is closed on Good Friday, Easter Sunday, Christmas Day, Boxing Day and New Year's Day

Admission:
Entry to the museum is free of charge

Practical Information:
The museum has disabled access

Experiences:

Lark Hill Place:
Many original shop fronts feature in this wonderful recreation of a typical northern street at the end of the 19th and beginning of the 20th century, which has been brought to life with authentic sounds. Visit the Blue Lion Pub, marvel at the pills and potions in the chemists window, compare the home comforts of the Victorian parlour to the worker's cottage.

Victorian Gallery:
Relax amid the splendour of the Victorians' passion for painting, pottery and fine furniture.

Temporary Exhibitions:
Enjoy a varied and lively programme of temporary exhibitions ranging from contemporary arts and crafts, archaeology and architecture, to documentary photography and social history.

Events and Activities:
There's a whole range of hands-on activities for all the family. Try out one of our games or quizzes, or get to grips with some unusual art materials in one of our creative sessions. There's drama, dance and music too. A full family-friendly programme runs during the school holidays.

King's Lynn Arts Centre

St. George's Guildhall, together with the Fermoy, Red Barn, Shakespeare Barn and Old Warehouse Galleries forms the King's Lynn Arts Centre. Although it has been used for many purposes, the theatrical associations of this 15th-century Guildhall are strongest. Shakespeare himself is said to have performed here.

These ancient buildings front King Street and are close to the Tuesday Market Place.

Activity Location:
East Anglia

Contact Details:
King's Lynn Arts Centre
T: 01553 764864
W: www.kingslynnarts.co.uk

Special Offer:
A 10% discount available to *Ultimate Gift Experience* readers to the range of films. Cannot be combined with any other discount, special offer or promotion.

Experiences:

King's Lynn Arts Centre is an intimate venue, hosting a programme of comedy, drama, music, dance, film and visual arts. Housed in one of England's oldest surviving Guildhalls, the centre brings this historic building to life with its range of presentations in the main auditorium.

The complex also houses four art galleries that host a year-round programme of exhibitions, plus regular art, craft and education workshops, together with lectures on various art subjects.

The visitor can also explore their own artistic potential at one of the courses or workshops run by the centre.

★ **10% DISCOUNT** Please mention *Ultimate Gift Experiences* when booking

Wetheriggs Country Pottery

One of the few steam powered potteries left in Britain, Wetheriggs is a 19th century industrial monument. The pottery was founded in the 1860s, restored in the mid 1990s and is steeped in a history of incredible spirit and endeavour. Guided tours are available all year round and you can see designer makers at work. There are 7.5 acres of things to do, including the Pots of Fun Studio, the Pottery Museum, play areas, grounds and gardens, including a newt pond.

Activity Location:
South West

Contact Details:
Wetheriggs Country Pottery
T: 01768 892733
E: info@wetheriggs-pottery.co.uk
W: www.wetheriggs-pottery.co.uk

Experiences:

Activities include the following.

Designer Makers:
Wetheriggs has always been a home for artisans and crafts people including Interlude Ceramics by Mary Chappelhow. Mary not only creates the world famous Wetheriggs pottery, but designs her own unique contemporary ranges of stoneware. Other designer makers on-site include artists, jewellers, traditional wooden workshops, glass blowing, hand made gifts, pine craftsmen, stationery items and soft furnishings.

The visitor is very welcome to watch all designer makers at work and they all sell their creations, so the purchaser can take home a unique piece of artistry.

Pots of Fun Studio:
With no barriers of age or experience, the visitor can choose from throwing a pot from a nice wet juicy ball of clay, painting a figurine or bowl, creating a mosaic or painting on glass. Your imagination and our help can create a very personal piece of art for yourself or a precious gift for someone else.

Wetheriggs Country Pottery also run evening classes and daytime courses as well as 'Have a Go' Children's Parties.

Coaches and group bookings are also catered for by prior arrangement.

Stoke on Trent Museums

The North Staffordshire Potteries are the only area in the UK to be so closely identified with one industry. Ceramic production has shaped the economic life and the landscape of Stoke-on-Trent in a unique way. The ceramics collection at The Potteries Museum & Art Gallery is of national and international significance.

The other key collections at the branch museums help everyone enjoy and understand the heritage of the region, its industries, natural surroundings and people.

Activity Location:
Stoke on Trent

Contact Details:
Stoke on Trent Museums
T: 01782 232323
E: museums@stoke.gov.uk
W: www.stoke.gov.uk/museums

Additional Information:
Opening times vary between summer and winter
Admission prices vary

Experiences:

Museums include:

- *Potteries Museum & Art Gallery.* Travel back in time and discover the history of the potteries, including the world's greatest collection of Staffordshire ceramics. Displays include natural, local and archaeological history from in and around the potteries and a Mark XVI Spitfire commemorating its locally born designer Reginald Mitchell
- *Gladstone Pottery Museum.* Gladstone is the only complete Victorian Pottery Factory from the days when coal-burning ovens made the world's finest bone china. Traditional skills, original workshops, the cobbled yard and huge bottle kilns create an atmospheric time-warp
- *Etruria Industrial Museum.* The museum is the last steam-powered potters' mill in Britain. It includes Jesse Shirley's Bone & Flint Mill, scheduled as an ancient monument in 1975. The mill is 'in steam' seven times a year when the 1903 boiler is fired and historic machinery can be seen working
- *Ford Green Hall.* Home to the Ford family for nearly 200 years, Ford Green Hall is a 17th-century timber-framed farmhouse, complete with period gardens. The hall offers a fascinating insight into the life of the 17th century, with all rooms furnished with an outstanding collection of textiles, ceramics and furniture

Yorkshire Sculpture Park

Changing exhibitions in 500 acres of historic grounds and gardens bringing together art and nature. This beautiful, 18th-century landscape displays the best examples of modern and contemporary sculpture. Four indoor galleries also show a variety of exhibitions by international artists. The award-winning YSP Centre offers relaxing all-weather facilities. Enjoy a cappuccino in the coffee bar or a light lunch in the first-floor restaurant overlooking the parkland and sculpture or purchase designer craft, jewellery, gifts and books in the YSP shop.

Experiences:

Organised Talks and Tours:
A series of talks and tours, covering YSP activities, including exhibitions, landscape and heritage.

Education:
Using YSP's outdoor workshop spaces you can find an exciting programme of sculpture workshops, practical hands on sculpture courses, study days, lectures, outreach projects and school visits.

Activity Location:
Yorkshire

Contact Details:
Yorkshire Sculpture Park
T: 01924 832631
E: info@ysp.co.uk
W: www.ysp.co.uk

Additional Information:
The YSP Centre is available for exclusive corporate/private hire. Facilities include auditorium, boardroom and restaurant

The Geffrye Museum

The Geffrye Museum depicts the quintessential style of English middle-class living rooms. Its collections of furniture, textiles, paintings and decorative arts are displayed in a series of period rooms from 1600 to the present day, which lead the visitor on a walk through time.

The museum is set in elegant 18th-century almshouses with a contemporary wing surrounded by attractive gardens, which include an award-winning walled herb garden and a series of period gardens.

Activity Location:
London

Contact Details:
Geffrye Museum
T: 0207 7399893
E: info@geffrye-museum.org.uk
W: www.geffrye-museum.org.uk

Opening Times:
Tuesday–Saturday: 10am–5pm
Sundays & Bank Holidays: 12 noon–5pm
Closed Mondays (unless Bank Holiday Monday), Good Friday, Christmas Eve, Christmas Day, Boxing Day and New Year's Day

Experiences:

The museum has a range of facilities for visitors including:

- Walled herb garden and period garden rooms
- Restaurant
- Shop
- Special facilities for disabled visitors
- Lecture room and other areas available for hire

The Geffrye Museum is located in Shoreditch just minutes from the City of London. It is easily reached by public transport. Admission to the museum and gardens is free.

Otterton Mill

Set beside the River Otter in one of Devon's most beautiful valleys, and East Devon's magnificent World Heritage coast, Otterton Mill is a different kind of experience. A centuries-old working water mill, a famous bakery, shop and restaurant selling and serving local produce, and a gallery selling work from a selection of the best artists from Devon, Dorset and Somerset.

Experiences:

Bakery:
Otterton Mill has been using water power to produce stone-ground wholemeal flour for over a thousand years. This flour is used exclusively in the bakery, where it is hand baked, seven days a week into bread, cakes, shortbreads and the ever-popular scones.

Working Watermill:
There has been a working watermill at Otterton since Norman times. During the Middle Ages, Otterton Mill was one of the largest in Devon; however, during the mid-20th century, the mill fell into disrepair. It was restored in 1977, and once again began producing the wholemeal flour for which Otterton is so famous. There are numerous milling dates for visitors on the website.

Restaurant:
Open seven days a week, Otterton Mill Restaurant celebrates local culture and supports local producers, whether it's a simple snack, a wholesome lunch or an evening meal to accompany one of the Thursday evening music nights.

Activity Location:
Devon

Contact Details:
Otterton Mill
T: 01395 568521
E: escape@ottertonmill.com
W: www.ottertonmill.com

Gift Vouchers:
Available to purchase anything from the bakery, gallery or restaurant

Additional Information:
Most artwork and some bakery goods can be bought through the online mail order service
School and group bookings can be catered for by prior arrangement
Details of Thursday Music Nights can be found on the website

Bank of England Museum

Having been in existence for more than 300 years the Bank of England has, unsurprisingly, accumulated a considerable number of items associated with its history. These items are grouped into 'collections' and some items are displayed in the museum where they are used to illustrate the history of the institution and its role at the centre of the UK economy.

Activity Location:
Central London

Contact Details:
Bank of England Museum
T: 020 7601 5545
E: museum@bankofengland.co.uk
W: www.bankofengland.co.uk/education/museum/index.htm

Opening Times:
Monday to Friday 10am–5pm (closed at weekends and Bank Holidays)

Practical Information:
Admission is free for everyone
Admission to temporary exhibitions, events and activities is free although there is usually a small charge for exhibition brochures
There are no parking facilities on site
There are no refreshments on site
Visitors with disabilities should notify the museum before visiting

Experiences:

Collections:
The historical displays include material drawn from the bank's own collections of books, documents, silver, prints, paintings, banknotes, coin and photographs. There is also a display of gold, including Roman and modern gold bars, alongside pikes and muskets once used to defend the bank. Computer technology and audio visual displays explain the bank's present role.

Talks:
The museum offers a variety of talks and presentations for groups of visitors. They are designed for people of all ages, interests and abilities. All the talks and presentations are free of charge and must be booked in advance.

Exhibitions:
Special exhibitions and events take place in the museum throughout the year. These range from exhibitions on aspects of the Bank of England's work and history, often including items from the bank's collections that are not on public display, to activities for children during school holidays.

National Space Centre, Leicester

The award-winning National Space Centre is the UK's largest attraction dedicated to space. From the minute you catch sight of the Space Centre's futuristic Rocket Tower, you'll be treated to hours of breathtaking discovery and interactive fun.

With six fully interactive galleries, Rocket Tower, Space Theatre, Boosters restaurant and Cargo Bay shop, the National Space Centre has something for all the family.

Activity Location:
Midlands

Contact Details:
National Space Centre
T: 0870 607 7223
E: info@spacecentre.co.uk
W: www.spacecentre.co.uk

Opening Times:
Open everyday 10am to 5pm (last entry 3.30pm)
Closed Mondays during school term time, Christmas Day, Boxing Day and New Years Day

Visitor Facilities:
400 parking spaces, wheelchair loan, complete access to all levels, changing facilities, shop, restaurant, picnic area (outside), lockers and conference rooms

Experiences:

- *Into Space*: Do you have what it takes to be an astronaut? Test your reaction times, stress levels and communication skills
- *Exploring the Universe*: From black holes to backyard astronomy and the search for intelligent life. Create your own alien and take a journey through a wormhole
- *The Planets*: Test drive a Martian Rover Robot, see a very rare piece of moon rock and visit the Sunshine Activity area for our littlest visitors
- *Orbiting Earth*: Explore the way we look at our dynamic and beautiful planet
- *Space Now*: Communicating the latest news in space!
- *Tranquillity Base*: The new fantastic experience that challenges you to become an astronaut of the future
- *Rocket Tower*: Containing the National Space Centre's biggest rockets
- *Space Theatre*: A totally unique 360° full dome experience
- *Team Building Days*: Join the crew in the Challenger Learning Centre and take a mission to our space station
- *Gallery Dinners*: A unique venue for parties, product launches and out of this world entertainment
- *Conference Rooms*: Tailor made corporate packages to your requirements
- *Private Hire*: You can take control of the whole centre for company days or even a film backdrop

Directory of activities

Ultimate Gift Experiences: Your guide to unusual, adventurous and once in a lifetime gifts is published by Infinite Ideas, creators of the acclaimed **52 Brilliant Ideas** series and a range of other titles which are all life-enhancing and entertaining. If you found this book of interest, you may want to take advantage of this special offer exclusive to all readers of *Ultimate Gift Experiences.* Choose any two books from the selection below and you'll get one of them free of charge*. See p.181 for prices and details on how to place your order.

Adventure sports
52 Brilliant Ideas for taking yourself to the limit
By Steve Shipside

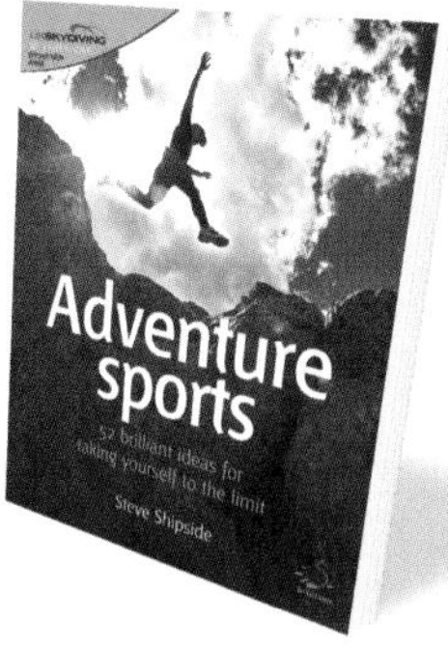

Skiing and snowboarding
52 Brilliant ideas for fun on the slopes
By Cathy Struthers

Getting away with it
Shortcuts to the things you don't really deserve
Compiled by Steve Shipside

Win at the gym
Secrets of fitness and health success
By Steve Shipside

Re-energise your sex life
(2nd edition) *52 Brilliant ideas to put the zing back into your lovemaking*
By Elisabeth Wilson

Stress proof your life
52 brilliant ideas for taking control
By Elisabeth Wilson

*If books vary in price we'll give you the lowest priced one free. Postage at £2.75 per delivery address is additional.

Upgrade your brain
52 brilliant ideas for everyday genius
By John Middleton

Podcasting
The ultimate starter kit
By Steve Shipside

Inspired creative writing
Secrets of the master wordsmiths
By Alexander Gordon Smith

Healthy cooking for children
52 brilliant ideas to dump the junk
By Mandy Francis

Unleash your creativity
Secrets of creative genius
By Rob Bevan & Tim Wright

Discover your roots
52 Brilliant Ideas for exploring your heritage
By Paul Blake & Maggie Loughran

Erotic fantasies
Brilliant ideas for raunchy role play
By Sandie Tifinie

Detox your finances
Secrets of personal finance success
By John Middleton

For more detailed information on these books and others published by Infinite Ideas please visit www.infideas.com

Choose any two titles from below and receive the cheapest one free:

Qty	Title	RRP
	Adventure sports	£12.99
	Skiing and snowboarding	£12.99
	Getting away with it	£6.99
	Win at the gym	£12.99
	Re-energise your sex life	£12.99
	Stress proof your life	£12.99
	Upgrade your brain	£12.99
	Podcasting	£7.99
	Inspired creative writing	£12.99
	Healthy cooking for children	£12.99
	Unleash your creativity	£12.99
	Discover your roots	£12.99
	Erotic Fantasies	£6.99
	Detox your finances	£12.99
	Subtract lowest priced book if ordering two titles	
	Add £2.75 postage per delivery address	
	Total	

Name:..

Delivery address:...

....

....

....

Email:...Tel: (in case of problems)...

By post: fill in all relevant details, cut out or copy this page and send along with a cheque made payable to Infinite Ideas. Send to: Ultimate Gift Offer, Infinite Ideas, 36 St Giles, Oxford OX1 3LD, UK.

Credit card orders over the telephone: call +44 (0) 1865 514 888. Lines are open 9am to 5pm Monday to Friday. Just mention the promotion code 'UGEAD06.'

Please note that no payment will be processed until your order has been dispatched. Goods are dispatched through Royal Mail within 14 working days, when in stock. We never forward personal details on to third parties or bombard you with junk mail. This offer is valid for UK and RoI residents only. Any questions or comments please contact us on 01865 514 888 or email info@infideas.com.

Free high speed sports car passenger ride worth at least **£30** for every *Ultimate Gift Experiences* reader

Is your inner speed freak wanting to break free? Now's your chance to get your fix in the fast lane. Infinite Ideas has teamed up with Direct Experiences to bring you this unique offer. As an Ultimate Gift Experiences reader you are entitled to one FREE high speed passenger ride at one of two premier driving venues in the UK.

In your free high speed ride you'll be driven by a professional racing driver in one of their latest racing cars around a purpose built track or circuit. You'll find out just how fast a supercar or rally car will accelerate and take a corner. Guaranteed to set your heart racing and get the adrenalin pumping.

Think these drivers are going to take it easy because you may be new to all this? Think again and hold tight. The thrill of one of these fast paced experiences is so unforgettable and exciting you really won't want it to end.

For more details on these experiences please see pages 58 and 60. Please see reverse on how to get your free high speed sports car passenger ride.

The voucher below entitles you to a high speed sports car passenger ride at either one of these premier venues for driving experiences:

Everyman Motor Racing at Prestwold Hall Circuit in Leicestershire
Telephone to book on 01455 841 670. Visit www.ferraridriving.com for more information.

Thruxton Motorsport Centre at Thruxton Circuit in Hampshire
Telephone to book on 01264 882 222. Visit www.thruxtonracing.co.uk for more information.

Once you have booked your date by phone you must complete the voucher below and return it to your chosen venue. Further details will be given at the time of booking.

For further details of the circuits please refer to the main entries on pages 58 and 60.

Free high speed sports car passenger ride voucher

This voucher entitles you to one FREE passenger ride.

Name:..

Address:..

Postcode:..

Tel No.:..

Date Booked:..

Venue:..

Voucher code DEPAS0607. Original vouchers only – no photocopies

Terms & conditions:

- Vouchers are valid until 1 December 2007 and not redeemable for cash. One ride per voucher.
- Offer subject to availability and is strictly on a first come, first served basis.
- Your FREE passenger ride must be booked and taken before 1 December 2007. Once booked you are unable to cancel or change your date. Cancellations will only be made by the venue in the case of extreme adverse weather conditions.
- This offer is only valid with the original voucher above. Photocopies will not be accepted.
- This offer takes place on specific weekdays at both venues, between 9.00 am and 3.00 pm. Please contact the venue for more details.
- It is essential you contact the venue beforehand to book your date.Your booking is not confirmed until you return your voucher.
- Late arrivals or attending on a non-operational date will mean you will not be able to receive your free ride.
- On the very rare occasion an event has to be cancelled on the day (e.g. extremely bad weather), you will be offered an alternative date.
- Spectators are welcome but animals are not permitted and a responsible adult must accompany children under 16 at all times.
- Participants must be over 18 years of age and will be asked to sign an indemnity on arrival. Third party insurance is included.
- Participants should be fit and healthy with no medical condition that would make this type of activity unsuitable, bearing in mind the high cornering and braking forces involved.
- Minimum height 5'; maximum height 6' 2"; maximum weight 15 stone.
- The venue reserves the right to offer a suitable alternative of equivalent cash value.